Name _____ Class _____

Concept Review

Section: Substances Are Made of Atoms

In the blank at the left of each word or phrase, write the letter of the expression on the right that is most closely related.

_____ **1.** atomic theory

a. This states that a chemical compound always contains the same elements in exactly the same proportions by weight or mass.

_____ **2.** law of definite proportions

b. This states that atoms are the building blocks of all matter.

_____ **3.** law of conservation of mass

c. This states that when two elements combine to form two or more compounds, the mass of one element that combines with a given mass of the other is in the ratio of small whole numbers.

_____ **4.** law of multiple proportions

d. This states that mass cannot be created or destroyed during ordinary chemical and physical changes.

Answer the following in the space provided.

5. State the five principles in Dalton's atomic theory.

a. _____

_____

b. _____

_____

c. _____

_____

d. _____

_____

e. _____

_____

Concept Review

Section: Structure of Atoms

In the blank at the left of each word or phrase, write the letter of the expression on the right that is most closely related.

_____ **1.** alpha particle   **a.** the electrode attached to the positive terminal of a voltage source

_____ **2.** anode   **b.** the electrode attached to the negative terminal of a voltage source

_____ **3.** atomic number   **c.** a subatomic particle that has a negative charge

_____ **4.** cathode   **d.** an atom's central region, which is made up of protons and neutrons

_____ **5.** Coulomb's law   **e.** a subatomic particle that has a positive charge and that composes the nucleus of an atom; the number of these particles determines the identity of an element.

_____ **6.** electron   **f.** the number of protons that compose the nucleus of an atom; this number is the same for all atoms of an element.

_____ **7.** proton   **g.** a subatomic particle that has no charge and that composes the nucleus of an atom

_____ **8.** isotope   **h.** a small, positively charged particle, which Rutherford directed at thin, gold foil

_____ **9.** mass number   **i.** the sum of the number of protons and neutrons of the nucleus of an atom

_____ **10.** neutron   **j.** states that the closer two charges are, the greater the force between them; in fact, the force increases by a factor of 4 as the distance is halved.

_____ **11.** nucleus   **k.** an atom that has the same number of protons (atomic number) as other atoms of the same element but has a different number of neutrons (atomic mass)

| Concept Review *continued*

Answer the following items in the space provided.

12. In Thomson's cathode-ray experiment, what evidence led him to believe that the ray consisted of particles, and why did he conclude that the ray was negatively charged?

_____

_____

_____

_____

13. Describe the evidence for the existence of electrons.

_____

_____

_____

14. Describe the evidence for the existence of protons.

_____

_____

_____

15. Describe the evidence for the existence of neutrons.

_____

_____

_____

16. Describe the properties of electrons, protons, and neutrons.

_____

_____

_____

17. In your own words, define *isotope*.

_____

_____

Name _____ Class _____ Date _____

| Concept Review *continued*

Use the appropriate term from the list below to fill in the blanks. Use each term only once.

volume	nucleus	small	alpha
positive	deflected	mass	undeflected

18. In the Rutherford gold foil experiment, positively charged _____

particles were directed at a thin gold foil. It was found that most of the

particles passed through the foil _____. However, a small number

of particles were _____, some even backward. These two

observations suggested that most of the _____ of an atom is

empty space but that there was a central core with a charge that repelled the

_____ particles. This core is a very _____ part of an

atom. It contains most of the _____ of the atom and is called the

_____.

19. Complete the following table.

Isotope	Number of protons	Number of electrons	Number of neutrons	Number of particles in nucleus	Symbol for isotope
Hydrogen-2					
Helium-3					
Lithium-7					
Beryllium-9					
Boron-11					

20. Define *atomic number* and *mass number*.

_____

_____

_____

_____

_____

Name _____ Class _____ Date _____

Skills Worksheet

Concept Review

Section: Electron Configuration

In the blanks at the left of each word or phrase, write the letter of the expression on the right that is most closely related.

_____ **1.** electromagnetic spectrum

_____ **2.** electron configuration

_____ **3.** excited state

_____ **4.** ground state

_____ **5.** Hund's rule

_____ **6.** line-emission spectrum

_____ **7.** orbital

_____ **8.** Pauli exclusion principle

_____ **9.** quantum number

_____ **10.** quantum theory

_____ **11.** aufbau principle

_____ **12.** photoelectric effect

a. the spectrum of a few colors seen through a prism made when high-voltage current is passed through a tube of hydrogen gas at low pressure

b. the lowest energy state of a quantized system

c. a state in which an atom has more energy than it does at its ground state

d. a number that specifies the properties of electrons in an atom

e. the arrangement of electrons in an atom

f. a region in an atom where there is a high probability of finding electrons

g. states that two particles of a certain class cannot be in the exact same energy state

h. the present-day model of the atom, in which electrons are located in orbitals

i. states that the structure of each successive element is obtained by adding one proton to the nucleus of the atom and one electron to the lowest-energy orbital that is available

j. all of the frequencies or wavelengths of electromagnetic radiation

k. what occurs when light strikes a metal and electrons are released

l. states that for an atom in the ground state, the number of unpaired electrons is the maximum possible and these unpaired electrons have the same spin

| Concept Review *continued*

Complete each statement below by writing the correct word or words in the spaces.

13. All electromagnetic radiation, including visible light, can be thought of as

moving _____.

14. As the frequency of a wave increases, the wavelength _____.

15. To define the region in which electrons can be found, scientists have assigned

four _____ numbers to each electron.

Answer the following items in the space provided.

16. Using the quantum theory, how does one determine the location of an atom's
electrons?

_____

_____

_____

_____

_____

_____

17. Compare the Rutherford, Bohr, and quantum models of an atom.

_____

_____

_____

_____

_____

_____

_____

_____

_____

_____

Concept Review *continued*

18. Explain how the wavelengths of light emitted by an atom provide information about electron energy levels.

_____

_____

_____

_____

19. List the four quantum numbers, and describe their significance.

_____

_____

_____

_____

_____

_____

_____

20. Use the Pauli exclusion principle and the aufbau principle to write the electron configuration for the following atoms.

a. Chlorine

b. Nitrogen

c. Calcium

Name _____ Class _____ Date _____

Concept Review

Section: Counting Atoms

In the blanks at the left of each word or phrase, write the letter of the expression on the right that is most closely related.

_____ **1.** Avogadro's number

_____ **2.** atomic mass

_____ **3.** mole

_____ **4.** molar mass

a. the mass of an atom expressed in atomic mass units

b. the SI base unit used to measure the amount of a substance whose number of particles is the same as the number of atoms in 12 grams of carbon-12

c. the mass in grams of one mole of a substance

d. the number of atoms or molecules in 1 mol, equal to 6.022×10^{23}

Answer the following items in the space provided.

5. Which isotope defines the atomic mass unit, and how is the atomic mass unit defined?

_____

_____

6. Why is a mole used to count atoms?

_____

_____

7. What is the relationship between an atom's atomic mass and one mole of that atom?

_____

_____

_____

Name _____ Class _____ Date _____

Concept Review *continued*

8. The atomic mass of lithium is 6.939 amu. Would you expect the isotopes ^6_3Li and ^7_3Li to be equally common? Why or why not? If not, which isotope would you expect to be more common?

_____

_____

_____

_____

_____

9. What is the mass in atomic mass units of one fluorine atom?

_____

10. What is the mass in grams of one fluorine atom?

11. How many molecules are in one mole of carbon dioxide, CO_2?

12. Calculate the mass of one mole of carbon dioxide, CO_2.

Quiz

Section: Substances Are Made of Atoms

In the space provided, write the letter of the term or phrase that best answers the question.

_____ **1.** According to the law of definite proportions, any two samples of water, H_2O,

    a. will be made up only of particles consisting of two atoms of hydrogen and one atom of oxygen.

    b. will have the same ratio of mass of hydrogen to mass of oxygen.

    c. will have a 2:1 ratio of mass of hydrogen to mass of oxygen.

    d. Both (a) and (b)

_____ **2.** The law that states that mass cannot be created or destroyed in ordinary chemical and physical changes is known as the law of

    a. conservation of mass.

    b. mass action.

    c. multiple proportions.

    d. definite composition.

_____ **3.** "When two elements combine to form two or more compounds, the mass of one element that combines with a given mass of the other element is in the ratio of small whole numbers." This statement is known as the law of

    a. conservation of mass.

    b. mass action.

    c. multiple proportions.

    d. definite composition.

_____ **4.** Which two compounds are examples of the law of multiple proportions?

    a. $FeCl_3$ and $Fe_2(SO_4)_3$

    b. O_2 and O_3

    c. CO and CO_2

    d. $FeCl_2$ and $Fe(NO_3)_2$

_____ **5.** The law of multiple proportions can be partly explained by the idea that

    a. elements can combine in only one way to form compounds.

    b. whole atoms of the same two elements combine to form different compounds.

    c. elements in a compound always occur in a 1:1 ratio.

    d. only atoms of the same element can combine.

Quiz *continued*

_____ **6.** The observation that the mass of carbon dioxide formed from the reaction of carbon and oxygen equals the combined masses of the carbon and oxygen that reacted supports the law of
   a. conservation of mass.
   b. mass action.
   c. multiple proportions.
   d. definite composition.

_____ **7.** An atomic theory based on scientific observations started about
   a. 400 BCE.
   b. 1800.
   c. 1900.
   d. 1930.

_____ **8.** Dalton's atomic theory helped explain the law of conservation of mass because it stated that atoms
   a. could not combine.
   b. could not be created or destroyed.
   c. all had the same mass.
   d. were invisible.

_____ **9.** Dalton's atomic theory does NOT support which of the following observations?
   a. Matter is neither created nor destroyed in chemical and physical changes.
   b. Atoms of most elements are made up of protons, neutrons, and electrons.
   c. NO and NO_2 are compounds of nitrogen and oxygen.
   d. Hydrogen atoms differ from oxygen atoms.

_____**10.** Dalton failed to recognize that substances can exist in the form
   a. AB.
   b. A_2B.
   c. A_2.
   d. AB_2.

Name _____ Class _____ Date _____

Quiz

Section: Structure of Atoms

In the space provided, write the letter of the term or phrase that best answers the question.

_____ 1. From observing that, within a cathode tube, cathode rays could move a paddle wheel placed in their path, scientists concluded that
  a. a magnetic field was produced.
  b. particles were passing from the cathode to the anode.
  c. there was a high-pressure gas within the tube.
  d. atoms are indivisible.

_____ 2. The rays produced in a cathode tube in early experiments were
  a. only affected by magnetic fields.
  b. only affected by electric fields.
  c. were emitted from the negative electrode.
  d. All of the above

_____ 3. The behavior of cathode rays led scientists to conclude that the rays were composed of
  a. energy.
  b. positively charged particles.
  c. negatively charged particles.
  d. uncharged particles.

_____ 4. Because cathodes made of different metallic elements produced cathode rays, scientists generalized that
  a. all atoms have electrons.
  b. atoms are indivisible.
  c. atoms carry a positive charge.
  d. electrons vary in charge.

_____ 5. Because most of the alpha particles in Rutherford's gold-foil experiments passed through the foil, he concluded that
  a. atoms were mostly empty space.
  b. atoms contained no charged particles.
  c. electrons formed the nucleus.
  d. atoms are indivisible.

_____ 6. Because a few alpha particles were deflected back from the foil in Rutherford's gold-foil experiments, he concluded that the particles were
  a. striking electrons.
  b. indivisible.
  c. repelled by tiny regions of high positive charge.
  d. magnetic.

Name _____ Class _____ Date _____

_____ **7.** Which of the following descriptions is *not* a characteristic of the nucleus of an atom?
  a. positively charged
  b. contains uncharged particles
  c. accounts for most of the atom's volume
  d. accounts for most of the atom's mass

_____ **8.** A neutral atom of $_{14}^{29}\text{Si}$
  a. has an atomic number of 29.
  b. contains a total of 43 electrons, protons, and neutrons.
  c. contains 15 protons and 14 neutrons.
  d. Both (a) and (c)

_____ **9.** Which of the following atoms contains the most neutrons?
  a. $_{20}^{43}\text{Ca}$
  b. $_{21}^{45}\text{Sc}$
  c. $_{22}^{49}\text{Ti}$
  d. $_{24}^{50}\text{Cr}$

_____**10.** Each of the three isotopes of hydrogen, hydrogen-1, hydrogen-2, and hydrogen-3,
  a. contains one neutron and one proton.
  b. contains at least one neutron.
  c. has one proton in its nucleus.
  d. is equally abundant.

Assessment

Quiz

Section: Electron Configuration

In the space provided, write the letter of the term or phrase that best answers the question.

_____ 1. Which of the following atomic models could be referred to as the "solar-system" model of the atom?
  a. Thompson's plum-pudding model
  b. Rutherford model
  c. Bohr model
  d. quantum model

_____ 2. According to the Bohr model of the atom, which particles are allowed to exist in any one of a number of energy levels.
  a. electrons
  b. protons
  c. neutrons
  d. Both (b) and (c)

_____ 3. Which of the following atomic models is also referred to as the "electron-cloud" model of the atom?
  a. Thompson's plum pudding model
  b. Rutherford model
  c. Bohr model
  d. quantum model

_____ 4. Which model was developed in an attempt to explain hydrogen's line-emission spectrum?
  a. Thompson's plum-pudding model
  b. Rutherford model
  c. Bohr model
  d. quantum model

_____ 5. The line-emission spectrum of an atom is caused by the energies released when electrons
  a. jump from a lower energy level to a higher energy level
  b. jump from a higher energy level to a lower energy level
  c. jump from the ground state to an excited state
  d. None of the above

_____ 6. Because excited hydrogen atoms always produced the same line-emission spectrum, scientists concluded that hydrogen
  a. had no electrons.
  b. did not release energy.
  c. released energy of only certain values.
  d. could only exist in the ground state.

_____ **7.** If electromagnetic radiation **A** has a lower frequency than electromagnetic radiation **B**, then, compared to **B**,
  a. the wavelength of **A** is shorter.
  b. the energy of **A** is lower.
  c. **A** is more particle-like.
  d. Both (a) and (c)

_____ **8.** Quantum numbers are sets of numbers that
  a. are characteristic only of the hydrogen atom.
  b. consist of multiples of 2.
  c. specify properties of electrons
  d. relate the energies of protons in the atomic nucleus.

_____ **9.** The statement that no two electrons in the same atom can have the same four quantum numbers is a restatement of
  a. Bohr's law
  b. Hund's rule.
  c. the aufbau principle.
  d. the Pauli exclusion principle.

_____ **10.** The electron configuration of $^{27}_{13}\text{Al}$ is
  a. $1s^2 2s^2 2p^6 3s^1 3d^2$.
  b. $1s^2 2s^2 2p^5 3s^2 3p^2$.
  c. [Ne] $3s^2 3p^1$.
  d. [Ne] $3s^1 3p^1 3d^1$.

Name _____ Class _____ Date _____

Quiz

Section: Counting Atoms

In the space provided, write the letter of the term or phrase that best answers the question.

_____ 1. In determining atomic mass units, the standard is the
   a. carbon-12 atom.
   b. carbon-14 atom.
   c. hydrogen-1 atom.
   d. oxygen-16 atom.

_____ 2. The atomic mass unit is used to express
   a. atomic mass.
   b. atomic mass number.
   c. atomic number.
   d. molar mass.

_____ 3. The atomic mass unit equals about
   a. 10^{-27} kg.
   b. 10^{-27} g.
   c. 10^{-8} kg.
   d. 10^{6} g.

_____ 4. The unit g/mol is the unit of
   a. atomic mass.
   b. molar mass.
   c. atomic mass number.
   d. atomic number.

_____ 5. The number of atoms in a mole of any element is called
   a. its atomic number.
   b. Avogadro's number.
   c. the molar mass number.
   d. the gram-atomic number.

_____ 6. If samples of two different elements each represent one mole,
   a. they are equal in mass.
   b. they contain the same number of atoms.
   c. their molar masses are equal.
   d. they have the same atomic mass.

Quiz *continued*

_____ **7.** Using a periodic table, find the identity of the element that has an atomic mass of 40.078 amu.
  a. C
  b. Ca
  c. Cr
  d. Cu

_____ **8.** Using a periodic table, determine which of the following quantities is *not* equivalent to 1.00 mol.
  a. 6.022×10^{23} carbon atoms
  b. 26.0 g Fe
  c. 79.9 g Br
  d. 65.4 g Zn

_____ **9.** A mass of 6.01 g $^{33}_{16}$S (with an atomic mass of 32.97 amu) contains
  a. 198 mol $^{33}_{16}$S.
  b. 0.376 mol $^{33}_{16}$S.
  c. 0.182 mol $^{33}_{16}$S.
  d. cannot be calculated because $^{33}_{16}$S is an isotope of sulfur.

_____ **10.** How many silver atoms are in 1.75 mol Ag?
  a. 1.99×10^{26}
  b. 1.05×10^{24}
  c. 3.44×10^{23}
  d. 1.05×10^{23}

Name _____ Class _____ Date _____

Assessment

Chapter Test

Atoms and Moles

In the space provided, write the letter of the term or phrase that best completes each statement or best answers each question.

_____ **1.** Which of the following orbital notations for phosphorus is correct?

a.

$1s$ ↑↓ $2s$ ↑↓ $2p$ ↑↓ ↑↓ ↑↓ $3s$ ↑↓ $3p$ ↑↓ ↑ □

b.

$1s$ ↑↓ $2s$ ↑↓ $2p$ ↑↓ ↑↓ ↑↓ $3s$ ↑↑ $3p$ ↑ ↑ ↑

c.

$1s$ ↑↓ $2s$ ↑↓ $2p$ ↑↓ ↑↓ ↑↓ $3s$ ↑↓ $3p$ ↑ ↑ ↑

d.

$1s$ ↑↓ $2s$ ↑↓ $2p$ ↑↓ ↑↓ ↑↓ $3s$ ↑↓ $3p$ ↑ ↑ □

_____ **2.** Atoms contain equal numbers of
   a. electrons and neutrons.
   b. protons and neutrons.
   c. protons and electrons.
   d. protons, electrons, and neutrons.

_____ **3.** The atomic symbol for beryllium, $^9_4$Be, indicates that the
   a. atomic number is 4.
   b. atomic number is 9.
   c. mass number is 4.
   d. atomic number is equal to $9 - 4$.

_____ **4.** Which of the following pairs of atomic symbols represent isotopes?
   a. ^{235}U and ^{238}U
   b. P_4 and P_8
   c. ^{32}P and ^{83}Pb
   d. ^{50}Sn and ^{51}Sb

Copyright © by Holt, Rinehart and Winston. All rights reserved.
Holt Chemistry   18   Atoms and Moles

_____ **5.** The atomic mass of an atom of carbon is 12, and the atomic mass of an atom of oxygen is 16. To produce CO, 16 g of oxygen can be combined with 12 g of carbon. To produce CO_2, 32 g of oxygen combine with 12 g of carbon. The ratio of the masses of oxygen is
  a. 1:1.
  b. 2:1.
  c. 1:2.
  d. 8:3.

_____ **6.** An electron for which $n = 4$ has more ____ than an electron for which $n = 2$.
  a. spin
  b. stability
  c. energy
  d. wave nature

_____ **7.** Rutherford's gold foil experiment led him to conclude that
  a. Thomson's plum pudding model of the atom was accurate.
  b. alpha particles were a poor choice for a bombardment material.
  c. a concentrated positive charge existed somewhere within the atom.
  d. light was emitted by electrons returning to ground state.

_____ **8.** Which of the following statements is *not* one of the five principles of Dalton's theory?
  a. Atoms of different elements combine in simple whole-number ratios to form compounds.
  b. All matter is made of indivisible, indestructible atoms.
  c. All atoms have similar physical and chemical properties.
  d. Chemical reactions consist of the combination, separation, or rearrangement of atoms.

_____ **9.** According to the law of definite composition, any two samples of KCl will have
  a. the same mass.
  b. slightly different molecular structures.
  c. different densities.
  d. the same ratio of elements.

_____ **10.** The diagram $\boxed{\uparrow\downarrow}$ shows two electrons with
  a. opposite spins.
  b. the same spin.
  c. different energies.
  d. the same energy.

_____11. According to the law of conservation of mass, when sodium, hydrogen, and oxygen react to form a compound, the mass of the compound will be ____ the masses of the individual elements.
   a. equal to
   b. greater than
   c. less than
   d. either less than or equal to

_____12. The deflection of cathode rays in Thomson's experiments gave evidence of the ____ nature of electrons.
   a. wave
   b. charged
   c. particle
   d. spinning

_____13. An atom of potassium has 19 protons and 20 neutrons. Its mass number is
   a. 9.
   b. 19.
   c. 20.
   d. 39.

_____14. Which of the following quantum numbers describes a *p*-orbital in the third energy level?
   a. $n = 3 \ l = 0 \ m = 0$
   b. $n = 3 \ l = 1 \ m = 0$
   c. $n = 3 \ l = -1 \ m = 0$
   d. $n = 4 \ l = 1 \ m = 0$

_____15. The electron configuration in **Figure 1** violates

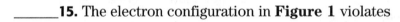
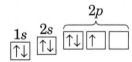

Figure 1

   a. the Pauli exclusion principle.
   b. the aufbau principle.
   c. Hund's rule.
   d. Both (a) and (c)

_____16. Light is emitted from a gaseous atom when an electron returns from a(n) ____ to its ground state.
   a. upper boundary
   b. excited state
   c. $n = 0$ state
   d. less energetic state

_____ **17.** One mole of iron atoms
   a. is more massive than one mole of aluminum atoms.
   b. is less massive than one mole of aluminum atoms.
   c. is a larger quantity of atoms than one mole of aluminum atoms.
   d. is a smaller quantity of atoms than one mole of aluminum atoms.

_____ **18.** Avogadro's number is
   a. 6.022×10^{23}.
   b. 1.602×10^{-24}.
   c. 3.1416.
   d. 3.0×10^{-8}.

_____ **19.** The molar mass of an element is numerically equal to the
   a. element's atomic mass.
   b. element's atomic number.
   c. number of neutrons found in the element.
   d. mass of one atom of the element.

_____ **20.** Using a periodic table, determine which of the following quantities
   contains the greatest number of atoms.
   a. 103.6 g Pb
   b. 2.0 mol Ar
   c. 0.1 mol Fe
   d. 4.0 g He

Answer the following questions in the spaces provided.

21. How does **Figure 2** illustrate the Pauli exclusion principle?

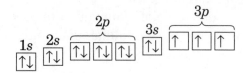

Figure 2

_____

_____

_____

_____

_____

_____

22. Describe how the atomic mass unit is operationally defined.

_____

_____

_____

_____

_____

_____

23. Discuss how Bohr's model of the atom builds on Rutherford's model.

_____

_____

_____

_____

_____

_____

_____

_____

Answer the following problems in the spaces provided. Show all calculations.

24. Using a periodic table, calculate the mass of a silver atom.
   (1 amu = $1.660\ 540\ 2 \times 10^{-27}$ kg)

25. How many wavelengths of light are represented in **Figure 3**?

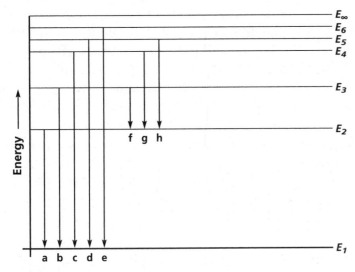

Figure 3

Skills Practice Lab

Flame Tests

Your company has been contacted by Julius and Annette Benetti. They are worried about some abandoned, rusted barrels of chemicals that their daughter found while playing in the vacant lot behind their home. The barrels have begun to leak a colored liquid that flows through their property before emptying into a local sewer. The Benettis want your company to identify the compound in the liquid. Earlier work indicates that it is a dissolved metal compound. Many metals, such as lead, have been determined to be hazardous to our health. Many compounds of these metals are often soluble in water and are therefore easily absorbed into the body.

Electrons in atoms jump from their ground state to excited states by absorbing energy. Eventually, these electrons fall back to their ground state, re-emitting the absorbed energy in the form of light. Because each atom has a unique structure and arrangement of electrons, each atom emits a unique spectrum of light. This characteristic light is the basis for the chemical test known as a flame test. In this test, the atoms are excited by being placed within a flame. As they re-emit the absorbed energy in the form of light, the color of the flame changes. For most metals, these changes are easily visible. However, even the presence of a tiny speck of another substance can interfere with the identification of the true color of a particular type of atom.

To determine what metal is contained in the barrels behind the Benettis' house, you must first perform flame tests with a variety of standard solutions of different metal compounds. Then you will perform a flame test with the unknown sample from the site to see if it matches any of the solutions you've used as standards. Be sure to keep your equipment very clean and perform multiple trials to check your work.

OBJECTIVES

Identify a set of flame-test color standards for selected metal ions.

Relate the colors of a flame test to the behavior of excited electrons in a metal ion.

Draw conclusions and identify an unknown metal ion by using a flame test.

Demonstrate proficiency in performing a flame test and in using a spectroscope.

MATERIALS

- beaker, 250 mL
- Bunsen burner and related equipment
- $CaCl_2$ solution
- cobalt-glass plates
- crucible tongs
- distilled water
- flame-test wire
- glass test plate, or a microchemistry plate with wells

- HCl solution (1.0 M)
- K_2SO_4 solution
- Li_2SO_4 solution
- Na_2SO_4 solution
- NaCl crystals
- NaCl solution
- spectroscope
- $SrCl_2$ solution
- unknown solution

Always wear safety goggles, gloves, and a lab apron to protect your eyes and clothing. If you get a chemical in your eyes, immediately flush the chemical out at the eyewash station while calling to your teacher. Know the location of the emergency lab shower and eyewash station and the procedures for using them.

Do not touch any chemicals. If you get a chemical on your skin or clothing, wash the chemical off at the sink while calling to your teacher. Make sure you carefully read the labels and follow the precautions on all containers of chemicals that you use. If there are no precautions stated on the label, ask your teacher what precautions to follow. Do not taste any chemicals or items used in the laboratory. Never return leftovers to their original container; take only small amounts to avoid wasting supplies.

Call your teacher in the event of a spill. Spills should be cleaned up promptly, according to your teacher's directions.

Acids and bases are corrosive. If an acid or base spills onto your skin or clothing, wash the area immediately with running water. Call your teacher in the event of an acid spill. Acid or base spills should be cleaned up promptly.

Do not heat glassware that is broken, chipped, or cracked. Use tongs or a hot mitt to handle heated glassware and other equipment because hot glassware does not always look hot.

When using a Bunsen burner, confine long hair and loose clothing. If your clothing catches on fire, WALK to the emergency lab shower and use it to put out the fire.

Name _____ Class _____ Date _____

| Flame Tests *continued*

Procedure

1. Put on safety goggles, gloves, and a lab apron.

2. Label a beaker "Waste." Thoroughly clean and dry a well strip. Fill the first well one-fourth full with 1.0 M HCl. Clean the test wire by first dipping it in the HCl and then holding it in the flame of the Bunsen burner. Repeat this procedure until the flame is not colored by the wire. When the wire is ready, rinse the well with distilled water, and collect the rinse water in the waste beaker.

3. Put 10 drops of each metal ion solution listed in the materials list except NaCl in a row in each well of the well strip. Put a row of 1.0 M HCl drops on a glass plate across from the metal ion solutions. Record the position of all of the chemicals placed in the wells. The wire will need to be cleaned thoroughly with HCl between each test solution to avoid contamination from the previous test.

4. Dip the wire into the $CaCl_2$ solution and then hold it in the flame of the Bunsen burner. Observe the color of the flame, and record it in the data table. Repeat the procedure again, but this time look through the spectroscope to view the results. Record the wavelengths you see from the flame. Perform each test three times. Clean the wire with the HCl as you did in step **2**.

5. Repeat step 4 with the K_2SO_4 and with each of the remaining solutions in the well strip. For each solution that you test, record the color of each flame and the wavelength observed with the spectroscope. After the solutions are tested, clean the wire thoroughly, rinse the well strip with distilled water, and collect the rinse water in the waste beaker.

6. Test another drop of Na_2SO_4, but this time view the flame through two pieces of cobalt glass. Clean the wire, and repeat the test using the K_2SO_4. View the flame through the cobalt glass. Record in your data table the colors and wavelengths of the flames. Clean the wire and the well strip, and rinse the well strip with distilled water. Pour the rinse water into the waste beaker.

7. Put a drop of K_2SO_4 in a clean well. Add a drop of Na_2SO_4. Flame-test the mixture. Observe the flame without the cobalt glass. Repeat the test, this time observing the flame through the cobalt glass. Record the colors and wavelengths of the flames in the data table. Clean the wire, and rinse the well strip with distilled water. Pour the rinse water into the waste beaker.

8. Test a drop of the NaCl solution in the flame, and then view it through the spectroscope. (Do not use the cobalt glass.) Record your observations. Clean the wire, and rinse the well strip with distilled water. Pour the rinse water into the waste beaker. Place a few crystals of NaCl in a clean well, dip the wire in the crystals, and do the flame test once more. Record the color of the flame test. Clean the wire, and rinse the well strip with distilled water. Pour the rinse water into the waste beaker.

| Flame Tests *continued*

9. Dip the wire into the unknown solution; then hold it in the Bunsen burner flame. Perform flame tests for the wire, both with and without the cobalt glass. Record your observations. Clean the wire, and rinse the well strip with distilled water. Pour the rinse water into the waste beaker.

10. Clean all apparatus and your lab station. Dispose of the contents of the waste beaker into the container designated by your teacher. Wash your hands thoroughly after cleaning up the lab area and equipment.

TABLE 1 FLAME TEST RESULTS

Metal Compound	Color of flame	Wavelengths (nm)
$CaCl_2$ solution		
K_2SO_4 solution		
Li_2SO_4 solution		
Na_2SO_4 solution		
$SrCl_2$ solution		
Na_2SO_4 (cobalt glass)		
K_2SO_4 (cobalt glass)		
Na_2SO_4 and K_2SO_4		
Na_2SO_4 and K_2SO_4 (cobalt glass)		
NaCl solution		
NaCl crystals		
Unknown solution		

Analysis

1. **Organizing data** Examine your data table, and create a summary of the flame test for each metal ion.

   _____

   _____

   _____

2. **Analyzing data** Account for any differences in the individual trials for the flame tests for the metal ions.

   _____

   _____

   _____

3. **Explaining events** Explain how viewing the flame through cobalt glass can make analyzing the ions being tested easier.

   _____

   _____

   _____

4. **Explaining events** Explain how the lines seen in the spectroscope relate to the position of electrons in the metal atom.

   _____

   _____

   _____

5. **Identifying patterns** For three of the metal ions tested, explain how the flame color you saw relates to the lines of color you saw when you looked through the spectroscope.

   _____

   _____

   _____

   _____

Conclusions

1. **Evaluating results** What metal ions are in the unknown solution from the barrels on the vacant lot?

_____

_____

_____

_____

2. **Evaluating methods** How would you characterize the flame test with respect to its sensitivity? What difficulties could occur when identifying ions by the flame test?

_____

_____

_____

_____

3. **Evaluating methods** Explain how you can use a spectroscope to identify the components of solutions containing several different metal ions.

_____

_____

_____

_____

4. **Applying ideas** Some stores sell jars of "fireplace crystals." When sprinkled on a log, these crystals make the flames blue, red, green, and violet. Explain how these crystals can change the flame's color. What ingredients would you expect the crystals to contain?

_____

_____

_____

_____

Extensions

1. **Designing experiments** A student performed flame tests on several unknown substances and observed that all of the flame colors were shades of red. What could the student do to correctly identify these substances? Explain your answer.

_____

_____

_____

_____

2. **Designing experiments** During a flood, the labels from three bottles of chemicals were lost. The three unlabeled bottles of white solids were known to contain the following substances: strontium nitrate, ammonium carbonate, and potassium sulfate. Explain how you could easily test the substances and relabel the three bottles. (Hint: Ammonium ions do not provide a distinctive flame color.)

_____

_____

_____

(Inquiry Lab)

Spectroscopy and Flame Tests–
Identifying Materials

January 27, 2004

Director of Investigations

CheMystery Labs, Inc.

52 Fulton Street

Springfield, VA 22150

Dear Director:

    As you may have seen in news reports, one of our freelance pilots, David Matthews, was killed in a crash of an experimental airplane. The reports did not mention that Matthews's airplane was a recently perfected design that he had been developing for us. The notes he left behind indicate that the coating on the nose cone was the key to the plane's speed and maneuverability.

    Unfortunately, he did not reveal what substances he used, and we were able to recover only flakes of material from the nose cone after the accident. We have sent you samples of these flakes dissolved in a solution. Please identify the material Matthews used so that we can duplicate his prototype. We will pay $200,000 for this work, provided that you can identify the material within three days.

Sincerely,

Jared MacLaren

Experimental Testing Agency

References

Review information about spectroscopic analysis. The procedure is similar to one used to identify an unknown metal in a solution. Use small amounts of metal, and clean equipment carefully to avoid contamination. Perform multiple trials for each sample.

The following information is the bright-line emission data (in nanometers) for the four possible metals.

- Lithium: 670, 612, 498, 462
- Potassium: 700, 695, 408, 405
- Strontium: 710, 685, 665, 500, 490, 485, 460, 420, 405
- Calcium: 650, 645, 610, 485, 460, 445, 420

Spectroscopy and Flame Tests—Identifying Materials *continued*

CheMystery Labs, Inc.
52 Fulton Street
Springfield, VA 22150

Memorandum

Date: January 28, 2004

To: Edwin Thien

From: Marissa Bellinghausen

We have narrowed down the material used to four possibilities. It is a compound of either lithium, potassium, strontium, or calcium. Using flame tests and the wavelengths of spectroscopic analysis, you should be able to identify which of these is in the sample.

Because our contract depends on timeliness, give me a preliminary report that includes the following as soon as possible:

- a detailed, one-page summary of your plan for the procedure, and

- an itemized list of equipment.

After you complete your analysis, prepare a report in the form of a two-page letter to MacLaren. The report must include the following:

- the identity of the metal in the sample,

- a summary of your procedure, and

- a detailed and organized analysis and data sections showing tests and results.

Spectroscopy and Flame Tests—Identifying Materials *continued*

Always wear safety goggles, gloves, and a lab apron to protect your eyes and clothing. If you get a chemical in your eyes, immediately flush the chemical out at the eyewash station while calling to your teacher. Know the location of the emergency lab shower and eyewash station and the procedures for using them.

Do not touch any chemicals. If you get a chemical on your skin or clothing, wash the chemical off at the sink while calling to your teacher. Make sure you carefully read the labels and follow the precautions on all containers of chemicals that you use. If there are no precautions stated on the label, ask your teacher what precautions to follow. Do not taste any chemicals or items used in the laboratory. Never return leftovers to their original container; take only small amounts to avoid wasting supplies.

Do not heat glassware that is broken, chipped, or cracked. Use tongs or a hot mitt to handle heated glassware and other equipment because hot glassware does not always look hot.

When using a Bunsen burner, confine long hair and loose clothing. If your clothing catches on fire, WALK to the emergency lab shower and use it to put out the fire. Do not heat glassware that is broken, chipped, or cracked. Use tongs or a hot mitt to handle heated glassware and other equipment because hot glassware does not always look hot.

When heating a substance in a test tube, the mouth of the test tube should point away from where you and others are standing. Watch the test tube at all times to prevent the contents from boiling over.

Call your teacher in the event of a spill. Spills should be cleaned up promptly, according to your teacher's directions.

Acids and bases are corrosive. If an acid or base spills onto your skin or clothing, wash the area immediately with running water. Call your teacher in the event of an acid spill. Acid or base spills should be cleaned up promptly.

Lesson Plan

Section: Substances Are Made of Atoms

Pacing

Regular Schedule   with lab(s): NA   without lab(s): 1 day
Block Schedule   with lab(s): NA   without lab(s): ½ day

Objectives

1. State the three laws that support the existence of atoms.

2. List the five principles of John Dalton's atomic theory.

National Science Education Standards Covered

UNIFYING CONCEPTS AND PROCESSES

UCP 1 Systems, order, and organization

UCP 2 Evidence, models, and explanation

UCP 5 Form and function

PHYSICAL SCIENCE—STRUCTURE OF ATOMS

PS 1a Matter is made of minute particles called atoms, and atoms are composed of even smaller components. These components have measurable properties, such as mass and electrical charge. Each atom has a positively charged nucleus surrounded by negatively charged electrons. The electric force between the nucleus and electrons holds the atom together.

PS 1b The atom's nucleus is composed of protons and neutrons, which are much more massive than electrons. When an element has atoms that differ in the number of neutrons, these atoms are called different isotopes of the element.

> **KEY**
> **SE** = Student Edition
> **ATE** = Annotated Teacher Edition

Block 1 *45 minutes*

FOCUS *10 minutes*

❑ **Bellringer,** ATE. This activity has students observe a sealed box containing a rattling object. Then they write down their inferences about the object and ways to learn about the object without opening the box.

MOTIVATE *5 minutes*

❑ **Discussion,** ATE (GENERAL). This activity asks students for an alternative to the model of matter in which atoms are the building blocks.

TEACH *25 minutes*

❏ **Transparency,** Law of Conservation of Mass (GENERAL). This transparency master shows that the total mass of a system remains the same whether atoms are combined, separated, or rearranged. (Figure 3)

❏ **Transparency,** Law of Multiple Proportions (GENERAL). This transparency master illustrates the law of multiple proportions using compounds of nitrogen and oxygen. (Table 1)

❏ **Misconception Alert,** ATE (GENERAL). This activity helps students distinguish between the law of multiple proportions and the law of definite proportions. Point out that the law of multiple proportions refers to two or more different compounds containing the same elements.

❏ **Inclusion Strategies,** ATE (GENERAL). This activity helps learning-disabled students and English-language learners practice and demonstrate their learning of the five principles of Dalton's atomic theory.

CLOSE *5 minutes*

❏ **Quiz,** ATE (GENERAL). This assignment has students answer questions about the concepts in this lesson.

❏ **Reteaching,** ATE (BASIC). Students create a concept map using the concepts in this section. Reproduce the best concept map on the chalkboard and use it for further discussion.

❏ **Interactive Tutor for ChemFile,** Module 2: Models of the Atom; Topic: Atomic Structure

❏ **Assessment Worksheet: Section Quiz** (GENERAL)

HOMEWORK

❏ **Reading Skill Builder,** ATE (BASIC). Have students list things that they already know about matter, atoms, and the particles that make up atoms.

❏ **Homework,** ATE (BASIC). This assignment provides students with a scrambled list of statements that they can match to the five principles of Dalton's atomic theory.

❏ **Section Review,** SE (GENERAL). Assign items 1–9.

❏ **Skills Worksheet: Concept Review** (GENERAL)

OTHER RESOURCES

❏ **History Connection,** ATE (ADVANCED). This activity has students research the work of alchemists and present their findings to the class.

❏ **Activity,** ATE (BASIC). This activity has students relate a beaker of boiling water to the particulate nature of matter.

❏ **go.hrw.com**

❏ **www.scilinks.org**

Lesson Plan

Section: Structure of Atoms

Pacing

Regular Schedule   **with lab(s):** NA   **without lab(s):** 2 days
Block Schedule   **with lab(s):** NA   **without lab(s):** 1 day

Objectives

1. Describe the evidence for the existence of electrons, protons, and neutrons, and describe the properties of these subatomic particles.

2. Discuss atoms of different elements in terms of their numbers of electrons, protons, and neutrons, and define the terms *atomic number* and *mass number*.

3. Define *isotope*, and determine the number of particles in the nucleus of an isotope.

National Science Education Standards Covered

UNIFYING CONCEPTS AND PROCESSES

UCP 1 Systems, order, and organization

UCP 2 Evidence, models, and explanation

UCP 5 Form and function

PHYSICAL SCIENCE—STRUCTURE OF ATOMS

PS 1a Matter is made of minute particles called atoms, and atoms are composed of even smaller components. These components have measurable properties, such as mass and electrical charge. Each atom has a positively charged nucleus surrounded by negatively charged electrons. The electric force between the nucleus and electrons holds the atom together.

PS 1b The atom's nucleus is composed of protons and neutrons, which are much more massive than electrons. When an element has atoms that differ in the number of neutrons, these atoms are called different isotopes of the element.

PHYSICAL SCIENCE—STRUCTURE AND PROPERTIES OF MATTER

PS 2b An element is composed of a single type of atom. When elements are listed in order according to the number of protons (called the atomic number), repeating patterns of physical and chemical properties identify families of elements with similar properties. This "Periodic Table" is a consequence of the repeating pattern of outermost electrons and their permitted energies.

KEY
SE = Student Edition
ATE = Annotated Teacher Edition

Block 2 *45 minutes*

FOCUS *5 minutes*

❏ **Bellringer** ATE (GENERAL). This activity has students write down the words that they do not know from the key terms.

MOTIVATE *10 minutes*

❏ **Identifying Preconceptions,** ATE (BASIC). This activity shows students that unexpected results can occur during experiments and can lead to new inquiry.

TEACH *30 minutes*

❏ **Demonstration,** ATE (GENERAL). This demonstration uses a television set and a magnet to demonstrate how a magnet held near a cathode ray tube causes the beam to be deflected. This phenomenon indicates that the particles in the beam have a negative charge. Compare this demonstration to Figure 6.

❏ **Transparency,** Gold-Foil Experiment (GENERAL). This transparency master shows the set up for the gold-foil experiment. (Figure 8)

❏ **Transparency,** Gold-Foil Experiment on the Atomic Level (GENERAL). This transparency master relates the results of the gold-foil experiment to the underlying atomic events. (Figure 8)

❏ **Using the Figure,** ATE (GENERAL). This activity has students examine the information in Table 3 and compare protons with neutrons.

HOMEWORK

❏ **Reading Skill Builder,** ATE (BASIC). Have students use Figure 6 and the information in their textbook to draw and label a diagram of a cathode ray tube.

❏ **Homework,** ATE (BASIC). This assignment has students create a graphic organizer using a question, discovery, and inference format.

OTHER RESOURCES

❏ **go.hrw.com**

❏ **www.scilinks.org**

| Lesson Plan *continued*

Block 3 *45 minutes*
TEACH *35 minutes*

❑ **Transparency,** Properties of Subatomic Particles (GENERAL). This transparency master summarizes the properties of electrons, neutrons, and protons. (Table 2 and Table 3)

❑ **Teaching Tip,** ATE (GENERAL). Show students a periodic table and point out the atomic numbers. This activity helps students realize that the numbers on a periodic table relate to the number of protons in each element's nucleus.

❑ **Sample Problem A: Determining the Number of Particles in an Atom,** SE (GENERAL). This problem demonstrates how to determine the number of particles in an atom.

❑ **Sample Problem B: Determining the Number of Particles of Isotopes,** SE (GENERAL). This problem demonstrates how to determine the number of particles in the isotopes of an element.

CLOSE *10 minutes*

❑ **Interactive Tutor for ChemFile,** Module 2: Models of the Atom; Topic: Atomic Structure

❑ **Quiz,** ATE (GENERAL). This assignment has students answer questions about the concepts in this lesson.

❑ **Reteaching,** ATE (BASIC). Students draw and label models of the nuclei of two isotopes.

❑ **Assessment Worksheet: Section Quiz** (GENERAL)

HOMEWORK

❑ **Practice Sample Problems A: Determining the Number of Particles in an Atom,** SE (GENERAL). Assign items 1–4.

❑ **Homework,** ATE (BASIC). Students complete a table to help them master the concepts of atomic number and mass number. (Sample Problem A)

❑ **Practice Sample Problems B: Determining the Number of Particles of Isotopes,** SE (GENERAL). Assign items 1–2.

❑ **Homework,** ATE (BASIC). This assignment provides students with additional practice in determining the number of particles in the isotopes of an element. (Sample Problem B)

❑ **Section Review,** SE (GENERAL). Assign items 1–8.

❑ **Skills Worksheet: Concept Review** (GENERAL)

OTHER RESOURCES

❏ **Skill Builder,** ATE (ADVANCED). Ask students to research the work going on in particle physics. Then, have them write a short paper about their findings.

❏ **Group Activity,** ATE (GENERAL). Small groups of students use $3'' \times 5''$ index cards to practice writing and reading nuclear symbols.

❏ **go.hrw.com**

❏ **www.scilinks.org**

Lesson Plan

Section: Electron Configuration

Pacing

Regular Schedule   **with lab(s):** 6 days   **without lab(s):** 2 days
Block Schedule   **with lab(s):** 3 days   **without lab(s):** 1 day

Objectives

1. Compare the Rutherford, Bohr, and quantum models of an atom.

2. Explain how the wavelengths of light emitted by an atom provide information about electron energy levels.

3. List the four quantum numbers, and describe their significance.

4. Write the electron configuration of an atom by using the Pauli exclusion principle and the aufbau principle.

National Science Education Standards Covered

UNIFYING CONCEPTS AND PROCESSES

UCP 1 Systems, order, and organization

UCP 2 Evidence, models, and explanation

UCP 5 Form and function

PHYSICAL SCIENCE—INTERACTIONS OF ENERGY AND MATTER

PS 6c Each kind of atom or molecule can gain or lose energy only in particular discrete amounts and thus can absorb and emit light only at wavelengths corresponding to these amounts. These wavelengths can be used to identify the substance.

KEY
SE = Student Edition
ATE = Annotated Teacher Edition

Block 4 *45 minutes*
FOCUS *5 minutes*

❏ **Bellringer,** ATE (GENERAL). Students sketch their concepts of the atom.

Lesson Plan *continued*

MOTIVATE *10 minutes*

❑ **Discussion,** ATE (GENERAL). Use students' models from the Bellringer above and their understanding of Rutherford's atomic model in Figure 15 to discuss the problems with Rutherford's model and set the stage for the concepts in this section.

TEACH *30 minutes*

❑ **Teaching Tip,** ATE (GENERAL). Show students either a CRT with a paddle-wheel or a photograph of one (for example, from the catalogue of a lab equipment company). Relate the piece of equipment to the experiment described in the textbook.

❑ **Transparency,** Electromagnetic Spectrum (GENERAL). This transparency master illustrates the electromagnetic spectrum. (Figure 18)

❑ **Using the Figure,** ATE (GENERAL). Use Figure 18 to review the parts of the electromagnetic spectrum. Make sure that students understand that the visible spectrum is a small part of the electromagnetic spectrum.

❑ **Transparency,** Wavelength and Frequency (GENERAL). This transparency master shows that frequency and wavelength are inversely related. (Figure 19)

❑ **Using the Figure,** ATE (GENERAL). Use Figure 19 and the questions in this feature to review the frequency and wavelength of red light and violet light.

HOMEWORK

❑ **Skill Builder,** ATE (BASIC). Have students look up the following terms in a dictionary: *quantum, quantum leap, quantum jump.* Then, have students relate the meanings of the terms to Bohr's atomic model.

❑ **Section Review,** SE (GENERAL). Assign items 1–3.

OTHER RESOURCES

❑ **Physics Connection,** ATE (ADVANCED). Ask students to research the work of Niels Bohr.

❑ **Teaching Tip,** ATE. Use a piece of rubber tubing or rope to demonstrate waves with differing wavelengths, frequencies, and amplitudes.

❑ **go.hrw.com**

❑ **www.scilinks.org**

| Lesson Plan *continued*

Block 5 *45 minutes*

TEACH *40 minutes*

❑ **Inclusion Strategies,** ATE (GENERAL). This activity helps learning disabled and developmentally delayed students as well as English language learners grasp the electromagnetic spectrum by having them draw and color a rainbow and label it with frequencies.

❑ **Transparency,** Hydrogen's Line Emission Spectrum (GENERAL). This transparency master shows hydrogen's emission spectrum. (Figure 20)

❑ **Using the Figure,** ATE (GENERAL). Compare the number of energy transitions shown in Figure 20 with the number of lines in the hydrogen spectrum, and discuss why these numbers are different.

❑ **Transparency,** Shapes of *s*, *p*, and *d* Orbital (GENERAL). This transparency master shows the shapes of the *s*, *p*, and *d* orbitals. (Figure 21)

❑ **Sample Problem C: Writing Electron Configurations,** SE (GENERAL). This problem demonstrates how to write electron configurations.

❑ **Datasheets for In-text Lab: Flame Tests,** SE (GENERAL). Students identify a set of flame-test color standards for selected metal ions and relate the colors of a flame test to the behavior of excited electrons in a metal ion. Then, students identify an unknown metal ion by using a flame test.

❑ **Datasheets for In-text Lab: Spectroscopy and Flame Tests,** SE (GENERAL). Students identify an unknown metal ion based on its flame test.

CLOSE *5 minutes*

❑ **Reteaching,** ATE (BASIC). Students write down one question relating to each heading and subheading in this section.

❑ **Quiz,** ATE (GENERAL). This assignment has students write the electron configurations of Sc, K, P, and B.

❑ **Assessment Worksheet: Section Quiz** (GENERAL)

HOMEWORK

❑ **Skill Builder,** ATE (ADVANCED). This activity has students calculate the wavelength in the first three transitions of the Lyman series.

❑ **Practice Sample Problems C: Writing Electron Configurations,** SE Assign items 1–2.

❑ **Homework,** ATE (BASIC). This assignment gives students additional practice writing electron configurations. (Sample Problem C).

❑ **Section Review,** SE (GENERAL). Assign items 3–11.

❑ **Skills Worksheet: Concept Review** (GENERAL)

❑ **Interactive Tutor for ChemFile,** Module 2: Models of the Atom; Topic: Electronic Structure

---

OTHER RESOURCES

❏ **Demonstration,** ATE (GENERAL). This demonstration shows students the emission spectra of different elements. It begins with the spectrum for hydrogen, which is also shown in Figure 20.

❏ **Skill Builder,** ATE (ADVANCED). Have students calculate the wavelength of the first three transitions in the Lyman series.

❏ **Focus on Graphing,** SE (GENERAL).

❏ **go.hrw.com**

❏ **www.scilinks.org**

Lesson Plan

Section: Counting Atoms

Pacing

Regular Schedule	**with lab(s):** NA	**without lab(s):** 2 days
Block Schedule	**with lab(s):** NA	**without lab(s):** 1 day

Objectives

1. Compare the quantities and units for atomic mass with those for molar mass.

2. Define *mole*, and explain why this unit is used to count atoms.

3. Calculate either mass with molar mass or number with Avogadro's number given an amount in moles.

National Science Education Standards Covered
UNIFYING CONCEPTS AND PROCESSES

UCP 1 Systems, order, and organization

UCP 2 Evidence, models, and explanation

UCP 5 Form and function

KEY   **SE** = Student Edition   **ATE** = Annotated Teacher Edition

Block 6 *45 minutes*
FOCUS *5 minutes*

❑ **Bellringer,** ATE (GENERAL). This activity has students write out the number of copper atoms calculated in regular notation, using all the zeroes needed as placeholders rather than in scientific notation.

MOTIVATE *10 minutes*

❑ **Discussion,** ATE (GENERAL). This activity uses the mass of a copper atom to walk students through the rationale and value of atomic mass units.

Lesson Plan *continued*

TEACH *30 minutes*

❑ **Group Activity,** ATE (BASIC). This activity has students observe a one-mole quantity of several substances and classify them as either an element or a compound.

❑ **Skills Toolkit: Determining the Mass from the Amount in Moles,** SE (GENERAL). Use this feature to walk students through the steps of calculating the mass of a substance using the amount of moles of a substance.

❑ **Transparency,** Determining the Mass by Using the Amount in Moles of a Substance (GENERAL). This transparency master illustrates how to calculate the mass of a substance using the amount of moles of a substance. (Skills Toolkit 1)

❑ **Reading Skill Builder,** ATE (BASIC). Have pairs of students read Section 4 and create a flowchart that describes how to solve two mole problems.

HOMEWORK

❑ **Teaching Tip,** ATE (GENERAL). To help students understand the value of Avogadro's number, have students calculate how many dollars each person in the world would get if a mole of dollars were evenly distributed among Earth's population.

❑ **Section Review,** SE (GENERAL). Assign items 1–5.

OTHER RESOURCES

❑ **Group Activity,** ATE (GENERAL). This activity has small groups of students devise an experiment to determine the number of beans in a package. Students are to apply the relationship between mass and moles.

❑ **go.hrw.com**

❑ **www.scilinks.org**

Block 7 *45 minutes*

TEACH *35 minutes*

❑ **Sample Problem D: Converting from Amount in Moles to Mass,** SE (GENERAL). This problem demonstrates how to convert from an amount in moles to mass.

❑ **Skills Toolkit: Determining the Number of Atoms from the Amount in Moles,** SE (GENERAL). Use this feature to walk students through the steps of calculating the number of atoms by using the amount of moles of a substance.

❑ **Sample Problem E: Converting from Amount in Moles to Number of Atoms,** SE (GENERAL). This problem demonstrates how to convert from moles to the number of atoms.

Lesson Plan *continued*

CLOSE *10 minutes*

❑ **Reteaching,** ATE (BASIC). Students create and solve their own problems based on Sample Problems D and E.

❑ **Quiz,** ATE (GENERAL). This assignment has students answer questions about the concepts in this lesson. Questions 4–6 are problems similar to Sample Problems D and E.

❑ **Assessment Worksheet: Section Quiz** (GENERAL)

HOMEWORK

❑ **Skills Worksheet: Concept Review** (GENERAL)

❑ **Practice Sample Problems D: Converting from Amount in Moles to Mass,** SE (GENERAL). Assign items 1–4.

❑ **Homework,** ATE (GENERAL). This assignment gives students additional practice converting from moles to mass. (Sample Problem D).

❑ **Practice Sample Problems E: Converting from Amount in Moles to Number of Atoms,** SE (GENERAL). Assign items 1–3.

❑ **Homework,** ATE (GENERAL). This assignment gives students additional practice converting from moles to number of atoms. (Sample Problem E).

❑ **Section Review,** SE (GENERAL). Assign items 6–13.

OTHER RESOURCES

❑ **go.hrw.com**

❑ **www.scilinks.org**

END OF CHAPTER REVIEW AND ASSESSMENT RESOURCES

❑ **Mixed Review,** SE (GENERAL).

❑ **Alternate Assessment,** SE (GENERAL).

❑ **Technology and Learning,** SE (GENERAL).

❑ **Standardized Test Prep,** SE (GENERAL).

❑ **Assessment Worksheet: Chapter Test** (GENERAL)

❑ **Test Item Listing for ExamView® Test Generator**

Skills Practice Lab

Flame Tests

Your company has been contacted by Julius and Annette Benetti. They are worried about some abandoned, rusted barrels of chemicals that their daughter found while playing in the vacant lot behind their home. The barrels have begun to leak a colored liquid that flows through their property before emptying into a local sewer. The Benettis want your company to identify the compound in the liquid. Earlier work indicates that it is a dissolved metal compound. Many metals, such as lead, have been determined to be hazardous to our health. Many compounds of these metals are often soluble in water and are therefore easily absorbed into the body.

Electrons in atoms jump from their ground state to excited states by absorbing energy. Eventually, these electrons fall back to their ground state, re-emitting the absorbed energy in the form of light. Because each atom has a unique structure and arrangement of electrons, each atom emits a unique spectrum of light. This characteristic light is the basis for the chemical test known as a flame test. In this test, the atoms are excited by being placed within a flame. As they re-emit the absorbed energy in the form of light, the color of the flame changes. For most metals, these changes are easily visible. However, even the presence of a tiny speck of another substance can interfere with the identification of the true color of a particular type of atom.

To determine what metal is contained in the barrels behind the Benettis' house, you must first perform flame tests with a variety of standard solutions of different metal compounds. Then you will perform a flame test with the unknown sample from the site to see if it matches any of the solutions you've used as standards. Be sure to keep your equipment very clean and perform multiple trials to check your work.

OBJECTIVES

Identify a set of flame-test color standards for selected metal ions.

Relate the colors of a flame test to the behavior of excited electrons in a metal ion.

Draw conclusions and identify an unknown metal ion by using a flame test.

Demonstrate proficiency in performing a flame test and in using a spectroscope.

Name _____ Class _____ Date _____

Flame Tests continued

MATERIALS

- beaker, 250 mL
- Bunsen burner and related equipment
- CaCl₂ solution
- cobalt-glass plates
- crucible tongs
- distilled water
- flame-test wire
- glass test plate, or a microchemistry plate with wells

- HCl solution (1.0 M)
- K₂SO₄ solution
- Li₂SO₄ solution
- Na₂SO₄ solution
- NaCl crystals
- NaCl solution
- spectroscope
- SrCl₂ solution
- unknown solution

 Always wear safety goggles, gloves, and a lab apron to protect your eyes and clothing. If you get a chemical in your eyes, immediately flush the chemical out at the eyewash station while calling to your teacher. Know the location of the emergency lab shower and eyewash station and the procedures for using them.

Do not touch any chemicals. If you get a chemical on your skin or clothing, wash the chemical off at the sink while calling to your teacher. Make sure you carefully read the labels and follow the precautions on all containers of chemicals that you use. If there are no precautions stated on the label, ask your teacher what precautions to follow. Do not taste any chemicals or items used in the laboratory. Never return leftovers to their original container; take only small amounts to avoid wasting supplies.

Call your teacher in the event of a spill. Spills should be cleaned up promptly, according to your teacher's directions.

Acids and bases are corrosive. If an acid or base spills onto your skin or clothing, wash the area immediately with running water. Call your teacher in the event of an acid spill. Acid or base spills should be cleaned up promptly.

Do not heat glassware that is broken, chipped, or cracked. Use tongs or a hot mitt to handle heated glassware and other equipment because hot glassware does not always look hot.

When using a Bunsen burner, confine long hair and loose clothing. If your clothing catches on fire, WALK to the emergency lab shower and use it to put out the fire.

Name _____ Class _____ Date _____

Flame Tests continued

Procedure

1. Put on safety goggles, gloves, and a lab apron.

2. Label a beaker "Waste." Thoroughly clean and dry a well strip. Fill the first well one-fourth full with 1.0 M HCl. Clean the test wire by first dipping it in the HCl and then holding it in the flame of the Bunsen burner. Repeat this procedure until the flame is not colored by the wire. When the wire is ready, rinse the well with distilled water, and collect the rinse water in the waste beaker.

3. Put 10 drops of each metal ion solution listed in the materials list except NaCl in a row in each well of the well strip. Put a row of 1.0 M HCl drops on a glass plate across from the metal ion solutions. Record the position of all of the chemicals placed in the wells. The wire will need to be cleaned thoroughly with HCl between each test solution to avoid contamination from the previous test.

4. Dip the wire into the $CaCl_2$ solution and then hold it in the flame of the Bunsen burner. Observe the color of the flame, and record it in the data table. Repeat the procedure again, but this time look through the spectroscope to view the results. Record the wavelengths you see from the flame. Perform each test three times. Clean the wire with the HCl as you did in step 2.

5. Repeat step 4 with the K_2SO_4 and with each of the remaining solutions in the well strip. For each solution that you test, record the color of each flame and the wavelength observed with the spectroscope. After the solutions are tested, clean the wire thoroughly, rinse the well strip with distilled water, and collect the rinse water in the waste beaker.

6. Test another drop of Na_2SO_4, but this time view the flame through two pieces of cobalt glass. Clean the wire, and repeat the test using the K_2SO_4. View the flame through the cobalt glass. Record in your data table the colors and wavelengths of the flames. Clean the wire and the well strip, and rinse the well strip with distilled water. Pour the rinse water into the waste beaker.

7. Put a drop of K_2SO_4 in a clean well. Add a drop of Na_2SO_4. Flame-test the mixture. Observe the flame without the cobalt glass. Repeat the test, this time observing the flame through the cobalt glass. Record the colors and wavelengths of the flames in the data table. Clean the wire, and rinse the well strip with distilled water. Pour the rinse water into the waste beaker.

8. Test a drop of the NaCl solution in the flame, and then view it through the spectroscope. (Do not use the cobalt glass.) Record your observations. Clean the wire, and rinse the well strip with distilled water. Pour the rinse water into the waste beaker. Place a few crystals of NaCl in a clean well, dip the wire in the crystals, and do the flame test once more. Record the color of the flame test. Clean the wire, and rinse the well strip with distilled water. Pour the rinse water into the waste beaker.

Flame Tests *continued*

9. Dip the wire into the unknown solution; then hold it in the Bunsen burner flame. Perform flame tests for the wire, both with and without the cobalt glass. Record your observations. Clean the wire, and rinse the well strip with distilled water. Pour the rinse water into the waste beaker.

10. Clean all apparatus and your lab station. Dispose of the contents of the waste beaker into the container designated by your teacher. Wash your hands thoroughly after cleaning up the lab area and equipment.

TABLE 1 FLAME TEST RESULTS

Metal Compound	Color of flame	Wavelengths (nm)
$CaCl_2$ solution	yellowish red (orange)	420, 455, 460, 485, 610, 645, 650
K_2SO_4 solution	violet (purple)	405, 408, 695, 700
Li_2SO_4 solution	red (carmine)	462, 498, 612, 670
Na_2SO_4 solution	yellow	590, 595
$SrCl_2$ solution	bright red (scarlet)	405, 420, 460, 485, 490, 500, 665, 685, 710
Na_2SO_4 (cobalt glass)	only the cobalt glass is visible	n.a.
K_2SO_4 (cobalt glass)	violet (purple)	n.a.
Na_2SO_4 and K_2SO_4	yellow	n.a.
Na_2SO_4 and K_2SO_4 (cobalt glass)	violet (purple)	n.a.
NaCl solution	yellow	590, 595
NaCl crystals	yellow	590, 595
Unknown solution	**Answers will vary**	**Answers will vary**

Name _____ Class _____ Date _____

Flame Tests *continued*

Analysis

1. **Organizing data** Examine your data table, and create a summary of the flame test for each metal ion.

   See sample data table. _____

   _____

   _____

2. **Analyzing data** Account for any differences in the individual trials for the flame tests for the metal ions.

   Answers will vary. Some students may have had difficulty cleaning the wire

   properly, so the first test of a new compound may have had traces of the

   previous compound.

3. **Explaining events** Explain how viewing the flame through cobalt glass can make analyzing the ions being tested easier.

   The flame color of potassium is purple, but it is so weak that it can be over-

   powered by the yellow sodium light if a mixture is tested. The cobalt glass

   screens out the yellow sodium light.

4. **Explaining events** Explain how the lines seen in the spectroscope relate to the position of electrons in the metal atom.

   Each line in the spectroscope represented the energy emitted as excited

   electrons   moved from a specific high-energy orbital back to their ground

   state.

5. **Identifying patterns** For three of the metal ions tested, explain how the flame color you saw relates to the lines of color you saw when you looked through the spectroscope.

   Answers will vary, but students should realize that the colors seen by the eye

   were the result of combining the colors of light seen in the line spectra.

   _____

Conclusions

1. **Evaluating results** What metal ions are in the unknown solution from the barrels on the vacant lot?

   <u>Answers will vary. Students should be able to identify the unknown by com-</u>

   <u>paring its results with those of the other metal compounds tested.</u>

2. **Evaluating methods** How would you characterize the flame test with respect to its sensitivity? What difficulties could occur when identifying ions by the flame test?

   <u>The flame test is fairly specific because it can show an easily detectable</u>

   <u>signal with a very small amount of material. Possible difficulties include</u>

   <u>problems with contamination and the fact that some metals have similar</u>

   <u>colors when flame tested.</u>

3. **Evaluating methods** Explain how you can use a spectroscope to identify the components of solutions containing several different metal ions.

   <u>The flame test of the mixture can be examined with the spectroscope. By</u>

   <u>comparing the lines in the spectra with those for other metals, one can</u>

   <u>determine which lines are due to which metals.</u>

4. **Applying ideas** Some stores sell jars of "fireplace crystals." When sprinkled on a log, these crystals make the flames blue, red, green, and violet. Explain how these crystals can change the flame's color. What ingredients would you expect the crystals to contain?

   <u>The crystals contain a mixture of metal salts. When sprinkled on a fire, the</u>

   <u>crystals cause the flame to show different colors, just as if several flame</u>

   <u>tests were being performed.</u>

Flame Tests *continued*

Extensions

1. **Designing experiments** A student performed flame tests on several unknown substances and observed that all of the flame colors were shades of red. What could the student do to correctly identify these substances? Explain your answer.

   The student should compare the red shades with those of the known

   samples. Information about spectral lines would also help determine which

   metal is the unknown.

   _____

2. **Designing experiments** During a flood, the labels from three bottles of chemicals were lost. The three unlabeled bottles of white solids were known to contain the following substances: strontium nitrate, ammonium carbonate, and potassium sulfate. Explain how you could easily test the substances and relabel the three bottles. (Hint: Ammonium ions do not provide a distinctive flame color.)

   Strontium nitrate will change the flame color to red; potassium sulfate will

   change the flame color to purple; and ammonium carbonate will not change

   the flame color.

Spectroscopy and Flame Tests–Identifying Materials

Teacher Notes

MATERIALS

- beaker, 250 mL
- Bunsen burner
- cobalt-glass plate
- crucible tongs
- flame-test wire (5 cm)

- glass plate, a 7 cm × 15 cm plate or a microchemistry well plate
- HCl solution, 1.0 M (5 mL)
- unknown solution (0.5 M Li_2SO_4 is recommended)

Optional Equipment

- spectroscope
- wooden splints

ANSWERS

Procedure

Place three drops of the unknown solution and several drops of 1.0 M HCl on a glass plate. Dip the flame-test wire in a drop of HCl to clean it. Dip the flame-test wire into the first drop of unknown solution. Hold the wire in a Bunsen burner flame, and record the color. (Record the wavelength as well, if a spectroscope is available.) Clean the wire in another drop of HCl, and repeat the process. When finished, rinse the plate with distilled water, and collect the rinse water in a waste beaker.

Estimated cost of materials: $86000 ($101 000 with spectroscope)

Sample Results

Substance	Unknown
Flame color	Red (carmine)
Wavelengths (nm)	462, 498, 612, 670

Student data should have multiple trials. Data is shown for Li_2SO_4. Data will vary if a different unknown is chosen.

Answer Key

Concept Review: Substances Are Made of Atoms

1. b
2. a
3. d
4. c
5. **a.** All matter is composed of extremely small particles called atoms, which cannot be subdivided, created, or destroyed.
   b. Atoms of a given element are identical in their physical and chemical properties.
   c. Atoms of different elements differ in their physical and chemical properties.
   d. Atoms of different elements combine in simple, whole-number ratios to form compounds.
   e. In chemical reactions, atoms are combined, separated, or rearranged but are never created, destroyed, or changed.

Concept Review: Structure of Atoms

1. h	7. e
2. a	8. k
3. f	9. i
4. b	10. g
5. j	11. d
6. c	

12. Thomson believed the rays were particles because a paddle wheel was set into motion by the ray. He concluded that the beam was negatively charged because the ray came from the negative electrode.

13. Thomson's experiments showed that a cathode ray consists of particles, called electrons, that have mass and a negative charge.

14. Positively charged particles in the nucleus, called protons, repel alpha particles in gold-foil experiments.

15. Protons and electrons have equal but opposite charges, but the mass of atoms is greater than the mass of the protons and electrons. Other particles, called neutrons (which have no electrical charge), accounted for the missing mass.

16. **electron:** a subatomic particle with a negative charge, found outside the nucleus
    proton: a subatomic particle with a positive charge, found in the nucleus
    neutron: a subatomic particle with no charge, found in the nucleus

17. Atoms of an element that have different numbers of neutrons are called isotopes.

18. alpha, undeflected, deflected, volume, positive, small, mass, nucleus

19. See completed table below.

Isotope	Number of protons	Number of electrons	Number of neutrons	Number of particles in nucleus	Symbol for isotope
Hydrogen-2	1	1	1	2	$_1^2\text{H}$
Helium-3	2	2	1	3	$_2^3\text{He}$
Lithium-7	3	3	4	7	$_3^7\text{Li}$
Beryllium-9	4	4	5	9	$_4^9\text{Be}$
Boron-11	5	5	6	11	$_5^{11}\text{B}$

20. atomic number: number of protons in the nucleus

mass number: number of particles in the nucleus

Concept Review: Electron Configuration

1. j
2. e
3. c
4. b
5. l
6. a
7. f
8. g
9. d
10. h
11. i
12. k
13. waves
14. decreases
15. quantum
16. Electrons within an energy level are located in orbitals. The quantum numbers tell the main energy level, the shape of the orbital, the orientation of the orbital, and the orientation of an electron's magnetic field.
17. Rutherford's electrons moved in circular orbits, like those of planets. Bohr's equations gave the regions of space, called orbitals, where the electrons were most likely to be found. The quantum model uses numbers to define the regions in which electrons are likely to be found.
18. Electrons release energy to move to lower energy levels. This energy is released as light that has a specific wavelength.
19. **principal quantum number:** indicates the main energy level occupied by an electron

angular momentum quantum number: indicates the shape of the orbital

magnetic quantum number: indicates the orientation of orbitals around the nucleus

spin quantum number: indicates the orientation of an electron's magnetic field relative to an outside magnetic field.

20. Chlorine: $1s^22s^22p^63s^23p^5$
Nitrogen: $1s^22s^22p^3$
Calcium: $1s^22s^22p^63s^23p^64s^2$

Concept Review: Counting Atoms

1. d
2. a
3. b
4. c
5. carbon-12; an amu is 1/12th of the mass of one carbon-12 atom.
6. A mole is used because working with great numbers can be difficult.
7. One mole of atoms has a mass in grams numerically equal to the atoms' mass in the atomic mass unit.
8. The atomic mass is the average of the atomic masses of naturally occurring isotopes. Since the atomic mass of lithium is nearly 7 amu, the mass of most atoms of lithium must be 7 amu and the mass of some atoms of lithium must be 6 amu. Therefore, lithium-7 must be a much more common isotope than lithium-6.
9. 18.9984 amu
10. 3.155×10^{-23} g
11. 6.022×10^{23}
12. 44.01 g

Answer Key

Quiz—Section: Substances Are Made of Atoms

1. d
2. a
3. c
4. c
5. b
6. a
7. b
8. b
9. b
10. c

Quiz—Section: Structure of Atoms

1. b
2. c
3. c
4. a
5. a
6. c
7. c
8. b
9. c
10. c

Quiz—Section: Electron Configurations

1. b
2. a
3. d
4. c
5. b
6. c
7. b
8. c
9. d
10. c

Quiz—Section: Counting Atoms

1. a
2. a
3. a
4. b
5. b
6. b
7. b
8. b
9. c
10. b

Chapter Test

1. c
2. c
3. a
4. a
5. c
6. c
7. c
8. c
9. d
10. a
11. a
12. b
13. d
14. b
15. c
16. b
17. a
18. a
19. a
20. b

21. According to the Pauli exclusion principle, no two electrons can have the same set of four quantum numbers. Therefore, no more than two electrons can occupy an orbital, and these two electrons must have opposite spins.

22. The atomic mass unit, or amu, is a mass equal to one-twelfth the mass of one carbon-12 atom.

23. Rutherford pictured the atom as having a central mass of positive charge around which the electrons moved in elliptical paths, or orbits. Bohr revised the model by showing that the electrons can occupy only certain energy levels, so their movement is in orbitals, or areas of probability, rather than in definite paths.

24. $107.9 \text{ amu} \times \dfrac{1.661 \times 10^{-27} \text{ kg}}{1 \text{ amu}} = 1.792 \times 10^{-25} \text{ kg}$

25. 8

MULTIPLE CHOICE

1. The law of conservation of mass follows from the concept that
   a. atoms are indivisible.
   b. atoms of different elements have different properties.
   c. matter is composed of atoms.
   d. atoms can be destroyed in chemical reactions.

   Answer: A   Difficulty: I   Section: 1   Objective: 1

2. The composition of the two oxides of lead, PbO and PbO_2, are explained by the
   a. periodic law.
   b. law of multiple proportions.
   c. atomic law.
   d. law of conservation of mass.

   Answer: B   Difficulty: II   Section: 1   Objective: 1

3. Who first proposed an atomic theory based on scientific knowledge?
   a. John Dalton
   b. Jons Berzelius
   c. Robert Brown
   d. Dmitri Mendeleev

   Answer: A   Difficulty: I   Section: 1   Objective: 2

4. According to Dalton's atomic theory, atoms
   a. are destroyed in chemical reactions.
   b. can be divided.
   c. of each element are identical in size, mass, and other properties.
   d. of different elements cannot combine.

   Answer: C   Difficulty: I   Section: 1   Objective: 2

5. Which of the following is NOT part of Dalton's atomic theory?
   a. Atoms cannot be divided, created, or destroyed.
   b. The number of protons in an atom is its atomic number.
   c. In chemical reactions, atoms are combined, separated, or rearranged.
   d. All matter is composed of extremely small particles called atoms.

   Answer: B   Difficulty: I   Section: 1   Objective: 2

6. The law of definite proportions
   a. contradicted Dalton's atomic theory.
   b. was explained by Dalton's atomic theory.
   c. replaced the law of conservation of mass.
   d. assumes that atoms of all elements are identical.

   Answer: B   Difficulty: I   Section: 1   Objective: 2

7. In a cathode tube, electrical current passes from one electrode, the _____, to the oppositely charged electrode.
   a. cathode
   b. anode
   c. negatively charged electrode
   d. Both (a) and (c)

   Answer: A   Difficulty: II   Section: 2   Objective: 1

8. Experiments with cathode rays led to the discovery of the
   a. proton.
   b. nucleus.
   c. neutron.
   d. electron.
   Answer: D   Difficulty: I   Section: 2   Objective: 1

9. Who explained the behavior of positively charged particles being deflected from a metal foil as the nucleus?
   a. Ernest Rutherford
   b. John Dalton
   c. James Chadwick
   d. Niels Bohr
   Answer: A   Difficulty: I   Section: 2   Objective: 1

10. In the gold foil experiment, most of the particles fired at the foil
    a. bounced back.
    b. passed through the foil.
    c. were absorbed by the foil.
    d. combined with the foil.
    Answer: B   Difficulty: I   Section: 2   Objective: 1

11. The gold foil experiment led to the discovery of the
    a. electron.
    b. cathode ray.
    c. nucleus.
    d. neutron.
    Answer: C   Difficulty: I   Section: 2   Objective: 1

12. What did Rutherford conclude about the structure of the atom?
    a. An atom is indivisible.
    b. Electrons make up the center of an atom.
    c. An atom carries a positive charge.
    d. An atom contains a small, dense, positively charged central region.
    Answer: D   Difficulty: I   Section: 2   Objective: 1

13. A nuclear particle that has about the same mass as a proton, but with no electrical charge, is called a(n)
    a. nuclide.
    b. neutron.
    c. electron.
    d. isotope.
    Answer: B   Difficulty: I   Section: 2   Objective: 1

14. Which part of an atom has a mass approximately equal to 1/2000 of the mass of a common hydrogen atom?
    a. nucleus
    b. electron
    c. proton
    d. electron cloud
    Answer: B   Difficulty: I   Section: 2   Objective: 1

15. The mass of a neutron is
   a. about the same as that of a proton.
   b. about the same as that of an electron.
   c. double that of a proton.
   d. double that of an electron.

   Answer: A   Difficulty: I   Section: 2   Objective: 1

16. The nucleus of most atoms is composed of
   a. tightly packed protons.
   b. tightly packed neutrons.
   c. tightly packed protons and neutrons.
   d. loosely connected protons and electrons.

   Answer: C   Difficulty: I   Section: 2   Objective: 1

17. Protons and neutrons strongly attract when they
   a. are moving fast.
   b. are very close together.
   c. are at high energies.
   d. have opposite charges.

   Answer: B   Difficulty: I   Section: 2   Objective: 1

18. An aluminum isotope consists of 13 protons, 13 electrons, and 14 neutrons. Its mass number is
   a. 13.
   b. 14.
   c. 27.
   d. 40.

   Answer: C   Difficulty: II   Section: 2   Objective: 2

19. Isotopes are atoms of the same element that have different
   a. principal chemical properties.
   b. masses.
   c. numbers of protons.
   d. numbers of electrons.

   Answer: B   Difficulty: I   Section: 2   Objective: 3

20. Atoms of the same element that have different masses are called
   a. moles.
   b. isotopes.
   c. nuclides.
   d. neutrons.

   Answer: B   Difficulty: I   Section: 2   Objective: 3

21. Isotopes of an element contain different numbers of
   a. electrons.
   b. protons.
   c. neutrons.
   d. nuclides.

   Answer: C   Difficulty: I   Section: 2   Objective: 3

22. When the light from excited atoms of an element is passed through a prism, the distinct colored lines produced are called
   a. ground states.
   b. excited states.
   c. line-emission spectra.
   d. electromagnetic spectra.

   Answer: C   Difficulty: I   Section: 3   Objective: 2

23. Bohr's theory helped explain why
    a. electrons have negative charge.
    b. most of the mass of the atom is in the nucleus.
    c. excited hydrogen gas gives off certain colors of light.
    d. atoms combine to form molecules.
    Answer: C   Difficulty: II   Section: 3   Objective: 2

24. According to Bohr's theory, an excited atom would
    a. collapse.
    b. absorb photons.
    c. produce line-emission spectra.
    d. radiate energy.
    Answer: D   Difficulty: II   Section: 3   Objective: 2

25. If electrons in an atom have the lowest possible energies, the electrons are in their
    a. ground states.
    b. inert states.
    c. excited states.
    d. radiation-emitting states.
    Answer: A   Difficulty: I   Section: 3   Objective: 2

26. For an electron in an atom to change from the ground state to an excited state,
    a. energy must be released.
    b. energy must be absorbed.
    c. radiation must be emitted.
    d. the electron must make a transition from a higher to a lower energy level.
    Answer: B   Difficulty: II   Section: 3   Objective: 2

27. Most of the volume of an atom is occupied by the
    a. nucleus.
    b. nuclides.
    c. electron cloud.
    d. protons.
    Answer: C   Difficulty: I   Section: 3   Objective: 2

28. The main energy levels of an atom are indicated by the
    a. orbital quantum numbers.
    b. magnetic quantum numbers.
    c. spin quantum numbers.
    d. principal quantum numbers.
    Answer: D   Difficulty: I   Section: 3   Objective: 3

29. The letter designations for the first four sublevels, with the number of electrons that can be accommodated in each sublevel are
    a. s: 1, p: 3, d: 10, and f: 14.
    b. s: 1, p: 3, d: 5, and f: 7.
    c. s: 2, p: 6, d: 10, and f: 14.
    d. s: 1, p: 2, d: 3, and f: 4.
    Answer: C   Difficulty: II   Section: 3   Objective: 3

30. The number of orbitals for the d sublevel is
    a. 1.
    b. 3.
    c. 5.
    d. 7.
    Answer: C   Difficulty: II   Section: 3   Objective: 3

31. The statement that an electron occupies the lowest available energy orbital is
    a. Hund's rule.
    b. the aufbau principle.
    c. Bohr's law.
    d. the Pauli exclusion principle.

    Answer: B   Difficulty: I   Section: 3   Objective: 4

32. "Orbitals of equal energy are each occupied by one electron before any is occupied by a second electron, and all electrons in singly occupied orbitals must have the same spin" is a statement of
    a. the Pauli exclusion principle.
    b. the aufbau principle.
    c. the quantum effect.
    d. Hund's rule.

    Answer: D   Difficulty: I   Section: 3   Objective: 4

33. The statement that no more than two electrons in the same atom can occupy a single orbital is
    a. the Pauli exclusion principle.
    b. Hund's rule.
    c. Bohr's law.
    d. the aufbau principle.

    Answer: A   Difficulty: I   Section: 3   Objective: 4

34. Which of the following rules requires that each of the p orbitals at a particular energy level receive one electron before any of them can have two electrons?
    a. Hund's rule
    b. the Pauli exclusion principle
    c. the aufbau principle
    d. the quantum rule

    Answer: A   Difficulty: I   Section: 3   Objective: 4

35. Two electrons in the $1s$ orbital must have different spin quantum numbers to satisfy
    a. Hund's rule.
    b. the magnetic rule.
    c. the Pauli exclusion principle.
    d. the aufbau principle.

    Answer: C   Difficulty: II   Section: 3   Objective: 4

36. The sequence in which energy sublevels are filled is specified by
    a. the Pauli exclusion principle.
    b. the orbital rule.
    c. Lyman's series.
    d. aufbau principle.

    Answer: D   Difficulty: I   Section: 3   Objective: 4

37. Which is the ground-state electron configuration for $_{24}$Cr ?

    a. [Ar] $4s^23d^4$
    b. [Ar] $4s^13d^5$
    c. [Ar] $4s^33d^3$
    d. [Ar] $4s^43d^2$

    Answer: B   Difficulty: III   Section: 3   Objective: 4

38. The carbon-12 atom is assigned a relative mass of exactly
    a. 1 amu.
    b. 6 amu.
    c. 12 amu.
    d. 100 amu.
    Answer: C   Difficulty: I   Section: 4   Objective: 1

39. The abbreviation for atomic mass unit is
    a. amu.
    b. mu.
    c. a.
    d. μ.
    Answer: A   Difficulty: I   Section: 4   Objective: 1

COMPLETION

40. The statement that a chemical compound always contains the same elements in exactly the same proportions is called the law of _____.
    Answer: definite proportions
    Difficulty: I   Section: 1   Objective: 1

41. The statement that mass cannot be created or destroyed in ordinary chemical and physical changes is called the law of _____.
    Answer: conservation of mass
    Difficulty: I   Section: 1   Objective: 1

42. The statement that when two elements combine to form two or more compounds, the mass of one element that combines with a given mass of the other element is in the ratio of small whole numbers is known as the law of _____.
    Answer: multiple proportions
    Difficulty: I   Section: 1   Objective: 1

43. A subatomic particle that has a negative electric change is a(n) _____.
    Answer: electron   Difficulty: I   Section: 2   Objective: 1

44. An atom's central region, which is made up of protons and neutrons, is the
    _____.
    Answer: nucleus   Difficulty: I   Section: 2   Objective: 1

45. A subatomic particle that has a positive charge and that is found in the nucleus of an atom is a(n) _____.
    Answer: proton   Difficulty: I   Section: 2   Objective: 1

46. A subatomic particle that has no charge and is found in the nucleus is a(n)
    _____.
    Answer: neutron   Difficulty: I   Section: 2   Objective: 1

47. The number of protons in the nucleus of an atom is called the _____.
    Answer: atomic number
    Difficulty: I   Section: 2   Objective: 2

48. The sum of the numbers of protons and neutrons of the nucleus of an atom is called the
    _____.
    Answer: mass number
    Difficulty: I   Section: 2   Objective: 2

49. An atom that has the same number of protons as other atoms of the same element but has a different number of neutrons is called a(n) _____.
    Answer: isotope   Difficulty: I   Section: 2   Objective: 3

50. Another method of writing the nickel isotope, $^{58}_{28}\text{Ni}$, is _____.

    Answer: nickel-58   Difficulty: I   Section: 2   Objective: 3

51. A region in an atom where there is a high probability of finding electrons is called a(n) _____.
    Answer: orbital   Difficulty: I   Section: 3   Objective: 1

52. Orbitals are sometimes called electron_____ because they do not have hard boundaries.
    Answer: clouds   Difficulty: I   Section: 3   Objective: 1

53. All of the frequencies or wavelengths of electromagnetic radiation make up the electromagnetic _____.
    Answer: spectrum   Difficulty: I   Section: 3   Objective: 2

54. The wavelength of electromagnetic radiation is inversely proportional to its_____.
    Answer: frequency   Difficulty: II   Section: 3   Objective: 2

55. Light can be thought of as a stream of particles, the _____ of which is determined by the light's frequency.
    Answer: energy   Difficulty: III   Section: 3   Objective: 2

56. A state in which an atom has more energy than it does in its ground state is called a(n) _____.
    Answer: excited state
    Difficulty: I   Section: 3   Objective: 2

57. A number that specifies a property of an orbital is called a(n) _____.
    Answer: quantum number
    Difficulty: I   Section: 3   Objective: 3

58. The statement that two particles of a certain class cannot be in the exact same energy state is known as the _____ principle.
    Answer: Pauli exclusion
    Difficulty: I   Section: 3   Objective: 4

59. The _____ of an atom is the arrangement of its electrons.
    Answer: electron configuration
    Difficulty: I   Section: 3   Objective: 4

60. The statement that the structure of each successive element is obtained by adding one proton to the nucleus of the atom and one electron to the lowest-energy orbital that is available is known as the _____ principle.
    Answer: aufbau   Difficulty: I   Section: 3   Objective: 4

61. The statement that for an atom in the ground state, the number of unpaired electrons is the maximum possible and these unpaired electrons have the same spin is known as _____ rule.
    Answer: Hund's   Difficulty: I   Section: 3   Objective: 4

62. The mass of an atom expressed in atomic mass units is the _____.
    Answer: atomic mass
    Difficulty: I   Section: 4   Objective: 1

63. The SI base unit used to measure the amount of a substance whose number of particles is the same as the number of particles in 12 g of carbon-12 is called the

_____.

Answer: mole   Difficulty: I   Section: 4   Objective: 2

64. Avogadro's number has a value (to three significant figures) of _____.

Answer: 6.02×10^{23} Difficulty: I   Section: 4   Objective: 2

65. The mass in grams of 1 mol of a substance is the substance's _____.

Answer: molar mass   Difficulty: I   Section: 4   Objective: 2

SHORT ANSWER

66. What is the atomic number of the atom $^{31}_{15}P$?

Answer: 15   Difficulty: I   Section: 2   Objective: 2

67. What is the mass number of the atom $^{86}_{36}Kr$?

Answer: 86   Difficulty: I   Section: 2   Objective: 2

68. How many electrons are in a neutral atom of $^{130}_{56}Ba$?

Answer: 56   Difficulty: I   Section: 2   Objective: 2

69. How many protons are in an atom of $^{91}_{40}Zr$?

Answer: 40   Difficulty: I   Section: 2   Objective: 2

70. How many neutrons are in an atom of $^{144}_{62}Sm$?

Answer: 82   Difficulty: I   Section: 2   Objective: 2

71. What is the molar mass of tin, which has an atomic mass of 118.7 amu?

Answer: 118.7 g/mol

Difficulty: I   Section: 2   Objective: 2

ESSAY QUESTIONS

72. Describe atomic mass.

Answer:

Atomic mass is the sum of the masses of the total number of protons and neutrons in the atom.

Difficulty: I   Section: 2   Objective: 2

73. Describe the atomic mass unit.

Answer:

The atomic mass unit is the average of the mass of the protons and neutrons in the carbon-12 isotope.

Difficulty: I   Section: 4   Objective: 1

74. How are the atomic mass unit and the atomic mass related?

Answer:

The atomic mass is the atomic mass unit multiplied by the number of protons and neutrons in the atom.

Difficulty: I   Section: 4   Objective: 1

PROBLEMS

75. What is the mass of 2.5 moles of carbon?
    Answer:

    $$2.5 \text{ moles C} \times \frac{12.01 \text{ g C}}{1 \text{ mol C}} = 3.0 \times 10^{1} \text{ g C}$$

    Difficulty: II   Section: 4   Objective: 3

76. How many moles of copper are present in 180.0 g Cu?
    Answer:

    $$180.0 \text{ g Cu} \times \frac{1 \text{ mol Cu}}{63.546 \text{ Cu}} = 2.833 \text{ moles Cu}$$

    Difficulty: II   Section: 4   Objective: 3

77. The mass of 1 mol of gold atoms is 196.97 g. Find the mass of 1 atom of gold.
    Answer:

    $$\frac{196.97 \text{ Au}}{1 \text{ mol Au}} \times \frac{1 \text{ mol Au}}{6.022 \times 10^{23}} = 3.27 \times 10^{-22} \text{ g / atom Au}$$

    Difficulty: III   Section: 4   Objective: 3

78. How many atoms are in 0.12 mol of cadmium?
    Answer:

    $$0.12 \text{ mol Cd} \times \frac{6.022 \times 10^{23} \text{ atoms Cd}}{1 \text{ mol Cd atoms}} = 7.3 \times 10^{22} \text{ atoms Cd}$$

    Difficulty: II   Section: 4   Objective: 3

Solutions Manual

Solutions for problems can also be found at go.hrw.com. Enter the keyword HW4ATSTNS to obtain solutions.

Practice Problems A

1. Given: atomic number of sodium = 11

Unknown: number of protons and electrons

atomic number = number of protons = number of electrons

For sodium, the atomic number = 11

number of protons = 11

number of electrons = 11

---

2. Given: element has 13 protons and 14 neutrons

Unknown: mass number

mass number = number of protons + number of neutrons

mass number = 13 + 14 = 27

---

3. Given: element has 45 neutrons and 35 electrons

Unknown: mass number

atomic number = number of protons = number of electrons

number of electrons = 35 = number of protons

mass number = number of protons + number of neutrons

mass number = 35 + 45 = 80

---

4. Given: element has 54 protons
(a) isotope has 77 neutrons
(b) isotope has 79 neutrons

Unknown: atomic number and mass numbers

atomic number = number of protons = number of electrons

number of protrons = 54

atomic number = 54

a. mass number = number of protons + number of neutrons
mass number = 54 + 77 = 131

b. mass number = number of protons + number of neutrons
mass number = 54 + 79 = 133

Practice Problems B

1. Given: atomic number of chlorine-35 and chlorine-37 = 17

Unknown: number of protons, electrons and neutrons for each isotope

atomic number = number of protons = number of electrons

mass number = number of protons + number of electrons

For Cl, the atomic number = 17

For Cl-35, the mass number = 35

For Cl-37, the mass number = 37

number of protons = 17

number of electrons = 17

number of neutrons = mass number − atomic number
= 35 − 17 = 18

number of neutrons = mass number − atomic number
= 37 − 17 = 20

Solutions Manual *continued*

2. Given: $^{42}_{20}Ca$ and $^{44}_{20}Ca$

    Unknown: number of protons, electrons and neutrons in each isotope

atomic number = number of protons = number of electrons

atomic number = 20

number of protons = 20

number of electrons = 20

$^{42}_{20}Ca$ mass number = number of protons + number of neutrons

number of neutrons = mass number − atomic number
= 42 − 20 = 22

$^{44}_{20}Ca$ mass number = number of protons + number of neutrons

number of neutrons = mass number − atomic number
= 44 − 20 = 24

Section 2 Review

4. Given: element with 22 electrons and 22 neutrons

    Unknown: nuclear symbol

atomic number = number of protons = number of electrons

number of electrons = 22

atomic number = 22

number of protons = 22

mass number = number of protons + number of neutrons

mass number = 22 + 22 = 44

$^{44}_{22}X$

5. Given: (a) $^{80}_{35}Br$
        (b) $^{106}_{46}Pd$
        (c) $^{133}_{55}Cs$

    Unknown: number of protons, electrons and neutrons

a. atomic number = number of protons = number of electrons

atomic number = 35

number of protons = 35

number of electrons = 35

mass number = number of protons + number of neutrons

number of neutrons = mass number − atomic number

number of neutrons = 80 − 35 = 45

b. atomic number = number of protons = number of electrons

atomic number = 46

number of protons = 46

number of electrons = 46

mass number = number of protons + number of neutrons

number of neutrons = mass number − atomic number

number of neutrons = 106 − 46 = 60

Solutions Manual *continued*

c. atomic number = number of protons = number of electrons

atomic number = 55

number of protons = 55

number of electrons = 55

mass number = number of protons + number of neutrons

number of neutrons = mass number − atomic number

number of neutrons = 133 − 55 = 78

---

6. Given: isotope with 56 electrons and 82 neutrons

Unknown: atomic number and mass number

atomic number = number of protons = number of electrons

number of electrons = 56

atomic number = 56

number of protons = 56

mass number = number of protons + number of neutrons

mass number = 56 + 82 = 138

Practice Problems D

1. Given: 1.00 mol of U

Unknown: mass of U in grams

$$1.00 \text{ mol U} \times \frac{238.03 \text{ g U}}{\text{mol U}} = 238. \text{ g U}$$

2. Given: 0.0050 mol U

Unknown: mass of U in grams

$$0.0050 \text{ mol U} \times \frac{238.03 \text{ g U}}{\text{mol U}} = 1.2 \text{ g U}$$

3. Given: (a) mass of H = 0.850 g
(b) amount of H = 0.850 mol

Unknown: (a) number of moles, (b) mass in grams

a. $0.850 \text{ g H} \times \frac{\text{mol H}}{1.01 \text{ g H}} = 0.84 \text{ mol H}$

b. $0.850 \text{ mol H} \times \frac{1.01 \text{ g H}}{\text{mol H}} = 0.86 \text{ g H}$

4. Given: (a) 2.3456 mol Pb
(b) 2.3456 g Pb

Unknown: (a) mass of Pb in grams
(b) number of moles

a. $2.3456 \text{ mol Pb} \times \frac{207.2 \text{ g Pb}}{\text{mol Pb}} = 486.0 \text{ g Pb}$

b. $2.3456 \text{ g Pb} \times \frac{\text{mol Pb}}{207.2 \text{ g Pb}} = 0.01132 \text{ mol Pb}$

Practice Problems E

1. Given: 0.70 mol Fe

Unknown: number of Fe atoms

$$0.70 \text{ mol Fe} \times \frac{6.022 \times 10^{23} \text{ Fe atoms}}{\text{mol Fe}} = 4.2 \times 10^{23} \text{ Fe atoms}$$

2. Given: 2.888×10^{23} Ag atoms

Unknown: amount of Ag

$$2.888 \times 10^{23} \text{ Ag atoms} \times \frac{\text{mol Ag}}{6.022 \times 10^{23} \text{ Ag atoms}} = 0.4796 \text{ mol Ag}$$

3. Given: 3.5×10^{23} Os atoms

Unknown: amount of Os

$$3.5 \times 10^{23} \text{ Os atoms} \times \frac{\text{mol Os}}{6.022 \times 10^{23} \text{ Os atoms}} = 0.58 \text{ mol Os}$$

Section 4 Review

6. Given: 3.01×10^{23} Si atoms

Unknown: amount of Si

$$3.01 \times 10^{23} \text{ Si atoms} \times \frac{\text{mol Si}}{6.022 \times 10^{23} \text{ Si atoms}} = 0.500 \text{ mol Si}$$

7. Given: 4.0 mol Na

Unknown: number of Na atoms

$$4.0 \text{ mol Na} \times \frac{6.022 \times 10^{23} \text{ Na atoms}}{\text{mol Na}} = 2.4 \times 10^{24} \text{ Na atoms}$$

8. Given: 118 g Co

Co = 58.93 amu

Unknown: amount of Co

$$118 \text{ g Co} \times \frac{\text{mol Co}}{58.93 \text{ g Co}} = 2.00 \text{ mol Co}$$

9. Given: 250 g Pt

Unknown: amount of Pt

$$250 \text{ g Pt} \times \frac{\text{mol Pt}}{195.08 \text{ g Pt}} = 1.3 \text{ mol Pt}$$

10. Given: 0.20 mol B

Unknown: grams of B, number of atoms

$$0.20 \text{ mol B} \times \frac{10.81 \text{ g B}}{\text{mol B}} = 2.2 \text{ g B}$$

$$0.20 \text{ mol B} \times \frac{6.022 \times 10^{23} \text{ atoms}}{\text{mol}} = 1.2 \times 10^{23} \text{ B atoms}$$

Chapter Review

37. Given: 1.00 mol H_2O

Unknown: number of water molecules

$$1.00 \text{ mol } H_2O \times \frac{6.022 \times 10^{23} \text{ } H_2O \text{ molecules}}{\text{mol } H_2O}$$

$$= 6.022 \times 10^{23} \text{ } H_2O \text{ molecules}$$

Solutions Manual *continued*

39. Given: atomic number
= 42
mass number = 96
Unknown: number of
neutrons

mass number = number of protons + number of neutrons

number of neutrons = mass number − atomic number

number of neutrons = 96 − 42 = 54

40. Given: atomic number of
Hg = 80, mass
number of
Hg = 201
Unknown: number of
electrons

atomic number = number of protons = number of electrons

atomic number = 80

number of electrons = 80

41. Given: mass number = 19
10 neutrons
Unknown: number of
protons

number of protrons = mass number − number of neutrons

= 19 − 10

= 9 protons

42. Given: mass number = 75
42 neutrons
Unknown: number of
electrons

atomic number = number of protons = number of electrons

number of protons = mass number − number of neutrons

= 75 − 42

= 33 protons

= 33 electrons

43. Given: atomic number of
U = 92, number of
neutrons for ura-
nium isotopes:
(a) 142
(b) 143
(c) 146
Unknown: nuclear
symbols

mass number = number of protons + number of neutrons

a. mass number = 92 + 142 = 234

b. mass number = 92 + 143 = 235

c. mass number = 92 + 146 = 238

a. uranium −234: $^{234}_{92}U$

b. uranium −235: $^{235}_{92}U$,

c. uranium −238: $^{238}_{92}U$

44. Given: atomic number
= 14, mass num-
ber of silicon's
three isotopes
Unknown: number of pro-
tons, neutrons
and electrons

atomic number = number of protons = number of electrons

atomic number = 14

number of protons = 14

number of electrons = 14

mass number = number of protons + number of neutrons

number of neutrons = mass number − atomic number

number of neutrons for Si-28 = 28 − 14 = 14

number of neutrons for Si-29 = 29 − 14 = 15

number of neutrons for Si-30 = 30 − 14 = 16

Solutions Manual *continued*

45. Given: 6 protons, isotopes: 6 neutrons,
7 neutrons

Unknown: symbols for
isotopes

mass number = number of protons + number of neutrons

mass number$_1$ = 6 + 6 = 12

mass number$_2$ = 6 + 7 = 13

$^{12}_{6}$C, $^{13}_{6}$C

46. Given: Ba has 56 protons,
isotopes: 74 neu-
trons, 81 neutrons

Unknown: symbols for
isotopes

mass number = number of protons + number of neutrons

mass number$_1$ = 56 + 74 = 130

mass number$_2$ = 56 + 81 = 137

$^{130}_{56}$Ba, $^{137}_{56}$Ba

51. Given: (a) 11.5 g of Na,
atomic mass of
22.99 amu
(b) 150 g of S,
atomic mass of
32.07 amu
(c) 5.87 g of Ni,
atomic mass of
58.69 amu

Unknown: amount of
each in mol

a. $11.5 \text{ g Na} \times \dfrac{\text{mol Na}}{22.99 \text{ g Na}} = 0.500 \text{ mol Na}$

b. $150 \text{ g S} \times \dfrac{\text{mol S}}{32.07 \text{ g S}} = 4.7 \text{ mol S}$

c. $5.87 \text{ g Ni} \times \dfrac{\text{mol Ni}}{58.69 \text{ g Ni}} = 0.100 \text{ mol Ni}$

52. Given: 2.50 mol Te

Unknown: mass in grams

$2.50 \text{ mol Te} \times \dfrac{127.60 \text{ g Te}}{\text{mol Te}} = 319 \text{ g Te}$

53. Given: amount of
H = 0.0050 mol

Unknown: mass in grams

$0.0050 \text{ mol H} \times \dfrac{1.01 \text{ g H}}{\text{mol H}} = 0.0050 \text{ g H}$

54. Given: 2.0 g H, atomic
mass = 1.01 amu

Unknown: number of
H atoms

$2.0 \text{ g H} \times \dfrac{\text{mol H}}{1.01 \text{ g H}} \times \dfrac{6.022 \times 10^{23} \text{ H atoms}}{\text{mol H}} = 1.2 \times 10^{24} \text{ H atoms}$

55. Given: (a) 2.0 mol Fe
(b) 40.1 g Ca,
atomic mass of
40.08 amu
(c) 4.5 mol of
boron-11

Unknown: number of
atoms present

a. $2.0 \text{ mol Fe} \times \dfrac{6.022 \times 10^{23} \text{ Fe atoms}}{\text{mol Fe}} = 1.2 \times 10^{24} \text{ Fe atoms}$

b. $40.1 \text{ g Ca} \times \dfrac{\text{mol Ca}}{40.08 \text{ g Ca}} \times \dfrac{6.022 \times 10^{23} \text{ Ca atoms}}{\text{mol Ca}}$

$= 6.03 \times 10^{23} \text{ Ca atoms}$

c. $4.5 \text{ mol B} \times \dfrac{6.022 \times 10^{23} \text{ B atoms}}{\text{mol B}} = 2.7 \times 10^{24} \text{ B atoms}$

56. Given: 7.85×10^{23} K
atoms

Unknown: amount of K

$7.85 \times 10^{23} \text{ K atoms} \times \dfrac{1 \text{ mol}}{6.022 \times 10^{23} \text{ atoms}} = 1.30 \text{ mol K}$

Solutions Manual *continued*

58. Given: (a) atom with 12 times mass of carbon-12

(b) atom with one-quarter mass of carbon-12

Unknown: atomic mass of given atoms

a. mass of carbon-12 = 12 amu
mass of given atom = (12)(12 amu) = 144 amu

b. mass of carbon-12 = 12 amu
mass of given atom = $\frac{1}{4}$(12 amu) = 3 amu

59. Given: 10.0 g B, atomic mass of B = 10.81 amu, atomic mass of Ag = 107.87

Unknown: mass of Ag containing the same number of atoms

$10.0 \text{ g B} \times \dfrac{\text{mol B}}{10.81 \text{ g B}} \times \dfrac{6.022 \times 10^{23} \text{ atoms B}}{\text{mol B}}$

$= 5.57 \times 10^{23}$ B atoms

$5.57 \times 10^{23} \text{ B atoms} \times \dfrac{1 \text{ Ag atom}}{1 \text{ B atom}} = 5.57 \times 10^{23}$ Ag atoms

$5.57 \times 10^{23} \text{ Ag atoms} \times \dfrac{\text{mol Ag}}{6.022 \times 10^{23} \text{ Ag atoms}} \times \dfrac{107.87 \text{ g Ag}}{\text{mol Ag}}$

$= 99.8$ g Ag

63. Given: (a) 3.5 mol C, atomic mass of 12.01 amu

(b) 5.0×10^9 Ne atoms, atomic mass of 20.18 amu

(c) 2.25×10^{22} C atoms, atomic mass of 12.01 amu

Unknown: mass in grams

a. $3.5 \text{ mol C} \times \dfrac{12.01 \text{ g C}}{\text{mol C}} = 42$ g C

b. $5.0 \times 10^9 \text{ Ne atoms} \times \dfrac{\text{mol Ne}}{6.022 \times 10^{23} \text{ Ne atoms}} \times \dfrac{20.18 \text{ g Ne}}{\text{mol Ne}}$

$= 1.7 \times 10^{-13}$ g

c. $2.25 \times 10^{22} \text{ C atoms} \times \dfrac{\text{mol C}}{6.022 \times 10^{23} \text{ C atoms}} \times \dfrac{12.01 \text{ g C}}{\text{mol C}}$

$= 0.449$ g

64. Given: 0.75 mol Np

Unknown: number of atoms

$0.75 \text{ mol Np} \times \dfrac{6.022 \times 10^{23} \text{ Np atoms}}{\text{mol Np}} = 4.5 \times 10^{23}$ Np atoms

68. Given: (a) 0.50 mol C
(b) 1.80 mol Ca

Unknown: mass in grams

a. $0.50 \text{ mol C} \times \dfrac{12.01 \text{ g C}}{\text{mol C}} = 6.0$ g C

b. $1.80 \text{ mol Ca} \times \dfrac{40.08 \text{ g Ca}}{\text{mol Ca}} = 72.1$ g Ca

69. Given: 5.50 mol Fe

Unknown: mass in kg

$5.50 \text{ mol Fe} \times \dfrac{55.85 \text{ g Fe}}{\text{mol Fe}} \times \dfrac{1 \text{ kg}}{1000 \text{ g}} = 0.307$ kg Fe

71. Given: 11 g of Si

Unknown: amount, number of atoms

$11 \text{ g Si} \times \dfrac{\text{mol Si}}{28.09 \text{ g Si}} = 0.39$ mol Si

$0.39 \text{ mol Si} \times \dfrac{6.022 \times 10^{23} \text{ atoms}}{\text{mol}} = 2.3 \times 10^{23}$ atoms

72. Given: 620 g of Li

Unknown: amount, number of atoms

$$620 \text{ g Li} \times \frac{\text{mol Li}}{6.94 \text{ g Li}} = 89 \text{ mol Li}$$

$$89 \text{ mol Li} \times \frac{6.022 \times 10^{23} \text{ atoms}}{\text{mol}} = 5.4 \times 10^{25} \text{ atoms}$$

73. Given: mass number = 11 amu, 5 electrons

Unknown: atomic number

atomic number = number of protons = number of electrons = 5

76. Given: 19.55 mol Au

Unknown: mass in grams

$$19.55 \text{ mol Au} \times \frac{196.97 \text{ g Au}}{\text{mol Au}} = 3851 \text{ g Au}$$

78. Given: 0.54 g He

Unknown: number of atoms

$$0.54 \text{ g He} \times \frac{\text{mol He}}{4.00 \text{ g He}} \times \frac{6.022 \times 10^{23} \text{ atoms}}{\text{mol}} = 8.1 \times 10^{22} \text{ He atoms}$$

Standardized Test Prep

5. Given: atomic number of Sn = 50

mass number of Sn = 119

Unknown: number of neutrons

mass number = number of protons + number of neutrons

number of neutrons = mass number – atomic number
= 119 – 50 = 69

Problem Bank

1. Given: name and mass number of bromine-80

Unknown: number of protons, electrons, and neutrons

atomic number = number of protons = number of electrons

mass number = number of neutrons + number of protons

For bromine, the atomic number = 35

For bromine-80, the mass number = 80

number of protons = 35 protons

number of electrons = 35 electrons

number of neutrons = mass number – atomic number = 80 – 35

number of neutrons = 45 neutrons

2. Given: name and mass number of carbon-13

Unknown: nuclear symbol for carbon-13

chemical symbol for carbon: C

atomic number for carbon = 6 (located at lower left of symbol)

mass number for carbon-13 = 13 (located at upper left of symbol)

carbon-13: $^{13}_{6}\text{C}$

3. Given: element that has 15 electrons and 15 neutrons

Unknown: hyphen notation for given element nuclide

atomic number = number of protons = number of electrons

mass number = number of protons + number of neutrons

atomic number = 15 (element is phosphorus)

mass number = 15 protons + 15 neutrons = 30

nuclide is phosphorus-30

4. Given: name and mass number of carbon-13

Unknown: number of protons, electrons, and neutrons

atomic number = number of protons = number of electrons

mass number = number of neutrons + number of protons

For carbon, the atomic number = 6

For carbon-13, the mass number = 13

number of protons = 6 protons

number of electrons = 6 electrons

number of neutrons = mass number – atomic number = 13 – 6

number of neutrons = 7 neutrons

5. Given: name and mass number of oxygen-16

Unknown: nuclear symbol for oxygen-16

chemical symbol for oxygen: O

atomic number for oxygen = 8 (located at lower left of symbol)

mass number for oxygen-16 = 16 (located at upper left of symbol)

oxygen-16: $^{16}_{8}O$

6. Given: element that has 7 electrons and 9 neutrons

Unknown: hyphen notation for given element nuclide

atomic number = number of protons = number of electrons

mass number = number of protons + number of neutrons

atomic number = 7 (element is nitrogen)

mass number = 7 protons + 9 neutrons = 16

16 nuclide is nitrogen-16

7. Given: 2.25 mol Fe

Unknown: mass of Fe in grams

$2.25 \text{ mol Fe} \times \dfrac{55.85 \text{ g Fe}}{\text{mol Fe}} = 125.663 \text{ g Fe} = 126 \text{ g Fe}$

8. Given: 0.375 mol K

Unknown: mass of K in grams

$0.375 \text{ mol K} \times \dfrac{39.10 \text{ g K}}{\text{mol K}} = 14.6625 \text{ g K} = 14.7 \text{ g K}$

9. Given: 0.0135 mol Na

Unknown: mass of Na in grams

$0.0135 \text{ mol Na} \times \dfrac{22.99 \text{ g Na}}{\text{mol Na}}$

$= 0.310365 \text{ g Na} = 0.3104 \text{ g Na}$

10. Given: 16.3 mol Ni
Unknown: mass of Ni
in grams

$$16.3 \text{ mol Ni} \times \frac{58.69 \text{ g Ni}}{\text{mol Ni}} = 956.647 \text{ g Ni} = 957 \text{ g Ni}$$

11. Given: 3.6 mol C
Unknown: mass of C
in grams

$$3.6 \text{ mol C} \times \frac{12.01 \text{ g C}}{\text{mol C}} = 43.236 \text{ g C} = 43 \text{ g C}$$

12. Given: 0.733 mol Cl
Unknown: mass of Cl
in grams

$$0.733 \text{ mol Cl} \times \frac{35.45 \text{ g Cl}}{\text{mol Cl}} = 25.9849 \text{ g Cl} = 26.0 \text{ g Cl}$$

13. Given: 5 g Ca
Unknown: amount of Ca
in moles

$$5 \text{ g Ca} \times \frac{\text{mol Ca}}{40.08 \text{ g Ca}} = 0.12475 \text{ mol Ca} = 0.1 \text{ g Ca}$$

14. Given: 3.6×10^{-10} g Au
Unknown: amount of Au
in moles

$$3.6 \times 10^{-10} \text{ g Au} \times \frac{\text{mol Au}}{196.97 \text{ g Au}}$$

$$= 1.82769 \times 10^{-12} \text{ mol Au} = 1.8 \times 10^{-12} \text{ mol Au}$$

15. Given: 3.22 g Cu
Unknown: amount of Cu
in moles

$$3.22 \text{ g Cu} \times \frac{\text{mol Cu}}{63.55 \text{ g Cu}}$$

$$= 0.0506688 \text{ mol Cu} = 0.051 \text{ mol Cu}$$

16. Given: 2.72×10^{-4} g Li
Unknown: amount of Li
in moles

$$2.72 \times 10^{-4} \text{ g Li} \times \frac{\text{mol Li}}{6.94 \text{ g Li}}$$

$$= 3.91931 \times 10^{-5} \text{ mol Li} = 3.92 \times 10^{-5} \text{ mol Li}$$

17. Given: 1.5×10^{12} Pb
atoms
Unknown: amount of Pb
in moles

$$1.5 \times 10^{12} \text{ Pb atoms} \times \frac{\text{mol Pb}}{6.022 \times 10^{23} \text{ Pb atoms}}$$

$$= 2.49087 \times 10^{-12} \text{ mol Pb}$$

18. Given: 2500 Sn atoms
Unknown: amount of Sn
in moles

$$2500 \text{ Sn atoms} \times \frac{\text{mol Sn}}{6.022 \times 10^{23} \text{ Sn atoms}}$$

$$= 4.1 \times 10^{-21} \text{ mol Sn}$$

19. Given: 2.75 mol Al
Unknown: number of
Al atoms

$$2.75 \text{ mol Al} \times \frac{6.022 \times 10^{23} \text{ Al atoms}}{\text{mol Al}}$$

$$= 1.66 \times 10^{24} \text{ Al atoms}$$

20. Given: 2.25×10^{22} C
atoms
Unknown: amount of C
in moles

$$2.25 \times 10^{22} \text{ C atoms} \times \frac{\text{mol C}}{6.022 \times 10^{23} \text{ C atoms}}$$

$$= 0.037 \text{ mol C}$$

21. Given: 2×10^6 O atoms
Unknown: amount of O
in moles

$$2 \times 10^6 \text{ O atoms} \times \frac{\text{mol O}}{6.022 \times 10^{23} \text{ O atoms}}$$

$$= 3 \times 10^{-18} \text{ mol O}$$

Solutions Manual *continued*

22. Given: 3.8 mol Na

Unknown: number of Na atoms

$$3.8 \text{ mol Na} \times \frac{6.022 \times 10^{23} \text{ Na atoms}}{\text{mol Na}}$$

$$= 2.3 \times 10^{24} \text{ Na atoms}$$

23. Given: 7.5×10^{15} Ni atoms

Unknown: mass of Ni in grams

$$7.5 \times 10^{15} \text{ Ni atoms} \times \frac{\text{mol Ni}}{6.022 \times 10^{23} \text{ Ni atoms}} \times \frac{58.69 \text{ g Ni}}{\text{mol Ni}}$$

$$= 7.3 \times 10^{-7} \text{ g Ni}$$

24. Given: 4 g S

Unknown: number of S atoms

$$4 \text{ g S} \times \frac{\text{mol S}}{32.07 \text{ g S}} \times \frac{6.022 \times 10^{23} \text{ S atoms}}{\text{mol S}}$$

$$= 7 \times 10^{22} \text{ S atoms}$$

25. Given: 9.00 g Al

Unknown: mass of Au with same number of atoms as 9.00 g Al

One mole of aluminum has the same number of atoms as one mole of gold. Therefore

1 mol Al = 1 mol Au

$$9.00 \text{ g Al} \times \frac{\text{mol Al}}{26.98 \text{ g Al}} \times \frac{\text{mol Au}}{\text{mol Al}} \times \frac{196.97 \text{ g Au}}{\text{mol Au}}$$

$$= 65.7 \text{ g Au}$$

26. Given: 5×10^9 Ne atoms

Unknown: mass of Ne in grams

$$5 \times 10^9 \text{ Ne atoms} \times \frac{\text{mol Ne}}{6.022 \times 10^{23} \text{ Ne atoms}} \times \frac{20.18 \text{ g Ne}}{\text{mol Ne}}$$

$$= 2 \times 10^{-13} \text{ g Ne}$$

27. Given: 0.02 g C

Unknown: number of C atoms

$$0.02 \text{ g C} \times \frac{\text{mol C}}{12.01 \text{ g C}} \times \frac{6.022 \times 10^{23} \text{ C atoms}}{\text{mol C}}$$

$$= 1 \times 10^{21} \text{ C atoms}$$

28. Given: 10 g B

Unknown: mass of Ag with same number of atoms as 10 g B

One mole of boron has the same number of atoms as one mole of silver. Therefore

1 mol B = 1 mol Ag

$$10 \text{ g B} \times \frac{\text{mol B}}{10.81 \text{ g B}} \times \frac{\text{mol Ag}}{\text{mol B}}$$

$$\times \frac{107.87 \text{ g Ag}}{\text{mol Ag}} = 100 \text{ g Ag}$$

29. Given: 3.25×10^5 g Pb

Unknown: amount of Pb in moles

$$3.25 \times 10^5 \text{ g Pb} \times \frac{\text{mol Pb}}{207.2 \text{ g Pb}}$$

$$= 1.57 \times 10^3 \text{ mol Pb}$$

30. Given: 150 g S

Unknown: amount of S in moles

$$150 \text{ g S} \times \frac{\text{mol S}}{32.07 \text{ g S}} = 4.7 \text{ mol S}$$